CHRISTIE'S

UNFORGETTABLE: FASHION OF THE Oscars®

NEW YORK
THURSDAY 18 MARCH 1999

TO BENEFIT amfAR
AIDS RESEARCH

SPONSORED BY VOGUE

CONTENTS

Cover: Elizabeth Taylor, escorted by Richard Burton, at the 1969 Academy Awards wearing LOT 53
© Copyright Academy of Motion Picture Arts and Sciences

CONTACTS FOR THIS SALE

For assistance and further information about this sale,
please contact the following:

Stacey Sayer   *Auction Coordinator*
Brenda Little   *Auction Administrator*

Tel   (212) 702 3709
Fax   (212) 446 9566

Absentee and Telephone Bids
For arrangement of bids for those
who cannot attend the sale:

New York:
Tel   (212) 546 1127
Fax   (212) 832 2216

London Client Services:
Tel   (44 171) 389 2414
Fax   (44 171) 925 2751

Payment
For buyer assistance on terms of payment:

Tel   (212) 546 1040
Fax   (212) 317 2439

or method of payment:

Tel   (212) 546 1124
Fax   (212) 759 7204

Shipping
For information on shipping of purchased property:

Tel   (212) 546 1113
Fax   (212) 980 8195

ADMISSION TO THE SALE

Owing to the anticipated interest in the sale, admission
to the auction will be limited to catalogue purchase and
ticket request only.

For a sale ticket please call (212) 546 5859
For a catalogue in the US please call (800) 395 6300
From outside the US please call (718) 784 1480

UNFORGETTABLE: FASHION OF THE Oscars®

AUCTION

Thursday 18 March 1999 at 6:00 p.m. (by ticket and catalogue only)
502 Park Avenue at 59th Street, New York, New York 10022

VIEWING

Thursday	11 March	10:00 a.m. – 5:00 p.m.
Friday	12 March	10:00 a.m. – 5:00 p.m.
Saturday	13 March	10:00 a.m. – 5:00 p.m.
Sunday	14 March	1:00 p.m. – 5:00 p.m.
Monday	15 March	10:00 a.m. – 5:00 p.m.
Tuesday	16 March	10:00 a.m. – 5:00 p.m.
Wednesday	17 March	10:00 a.m. – 2:00 p.m.

TOUR VIEWING

Sale Highlights

Christie's London
8 King Street, St. Jame's, London, England

| Tuesday | 23 February | 10:00 a.m. – 5:00 p.m. |
| Wednesday | 24 February | 10:00 a.m. – 2:00 p.m. |

Christie's Los Angeles
360 North Camden Drive, Beverly Hills, California

Friday	26 February	10:00 a.m. – 5:00 p.m.
Saturday	27 February	10:00 a.m. – 5:00 p.m.
Sunday	28 February	1:00 p.m. – 5:00 p.m.
Monday	1 March	10:00 a.m. – 5:00 p.m.

SALE CODE

In sending written bids or making inquiries, this sale should
be referred to as AMFAR–9074

This sale is subject to the Conditions of Business printed
at the back of this catalogue.

CHRISTIE'S

Janet Leigh and Tony Curtis at the 1959 Academy Awards.

DRESSING FOR OSCAR

HAMISH BOWLES
European Editor at Large, VOGUE

*T*he fashion gathered here is resonant with the excitement of the annual Academy Awards ceremony, charting the historic relationship between Hollywood, fashion, and celebrity. Over the decades since the awards were initiated in 1929, this relationship has proved by turns antipathetic or triumphantly symbiotic. The clothes often represent months of planning on the part of actress and designer, and vividly illustrate the changing codes of glamour. From the column of silvery beads that Edith Head created for Janet Leigh, a semaphore of high-voltage sex appeal as she arrived on the arm of husband Tony Curtis, at the 1959 Academy Awards ceremony (LOT 29), to the Olivier Theyskens and Jean Paul Gaultier outfit that Madonna wore in 1998 (LOT 32), announcing a new stage of street fashion awareness for the style chameleon, actresses and their designers have used the opportunity to communicate their messages to the movie-going public.

During the ascendancy of the studio system, actresses would be dressed and turned out for the Academy Awards and their attendant festivities by the studios' own costume and make-up departments. Over the years, many of the preeminent Hollywood costume designers left the studios to establish their own fashion houses, or ran these as a complement to their studio designing. The stars whose images they had helped to define remained loyal. The peerless Adrian, MGM's head designer, retired from the studio to open his own salon in 1941; his dresses were featured at the Academy Awards for the next decade until he closed his business. Paramount's Travis Banton and Howard Greer and MGM's Irene and Helen Rose (who designed Grace Kelly's 1956 wedding dress: MGM also gave the actress her Rose wardrobe from HIGH SOCIETY as part of her trousseau) all continued to dress Hollywood's actresses from their own dressmaking establishments. Jean Louis, Columbia Pictures' head designer, celebrated for the overtly sensuous gowns he created for pulchritudinous stars like Rita Hayworth, Lana Turner, and Kim Novak, continued to dress Hollywood's stars after he left to open his own salon. He even married one of them—Loretta Young, in 1993. Edith Head, however, remained a studio designer, working first with Paramount before joining Universal in 1968. Elizabeth Taylor chose the feisty eight-time Oscar® recipient to design the ballgown (LOT 53) that she wore to the 1969 Academy Awards (where she presented the Best Picture award to MIDNIGHT COWBOY). Their collaboration is brilliantly illustrative of the special talents that a studio designer, used to establishing a movie character's identity through clothing, could bring to dressing an actress for the Academy Awards. With its vast skirts and meticulously fitted low-cut bodice, the dress had nothing to do with contemporary high fashion but was instead designed to highlight the magnificent 69.42-carat diamond that Richard Burton had given her. The dress also accentuated Taylor's hand-span waist, voluptuous bosom, and, with its soft tonal play of hydrangea-blue-mauves, her legendary violet eyes (in Head's didactic 1967 book HOW TO DRESS FOR SUCCESS she had counseled "violet and purplish tones of blue" if your "Color Aura" matched Elizabeth Taylor's). Head and Taylor had collaborated on a visual projection of what the actress represented then as now—the paradigm of the great Hollywood star. Head is also represented through another star turn: Janet Leigh's 1960 (LOT 29) shining silver gown (Head also dressed Jane Wyman in a spangled sheath that year). Leigh's daughter Jamie Lee Curtis wore a dress that had belonged to Marlene Dietrich to the 1982 Academy Awards: Dietrich had worn the voluptuous gown in the 1942 movie THE LADY IS WILLING. Although Irene was Dietrich's accredited costumer on the production,

(right)
Edith Head won her 6th Academy Award for Best Black and White Costume Design for THE FACTS OF LIFE at the 1960 Academy Awards.

(left)
Marlene Dietrich rehearsing the musical finale *Strange Thing* for THE LADY IS WILLING, the 1942 Columbia comedy, directed and produced by Mitchell Leisen.

the dress itself was a Jean Louis creation—an early example of a relationship between actress and designer that would last for decades.

Although not a costume designer *per se*, Arnold Scaasi worked with Barbra Streisand on contemporary designs for ON A CLEAR DAY YOU CAN SEE FOREVER, and his emphatic and theatrical fashion statements made him a natural Oscar® night choice, although the black trouser suit that he made for Streisand for the 1968 awards caused a furor when she tripped on her way to the podium and it appeared to be transparent. "I thought we should show people she was a great modern girl," remembers Scaasi of the Streisand ensemble. "You were dressing the star according to her personality and you thought about it months before; you were an image to millions of people across the world." The designer accompanied Mitzi Gaynor, dressed by him in nude tulle spangled with beaded sunbursts (LOT 16), to the 1966 Academy Awards, and remembers that "it was a dazzling moment for me, surrounded by all the old movie stars—all these people I'd grown up with on the screen."

The flamboyant Bob Mackie is another costumer who was to establish himself as a fashion designer. After blue-chip apprenticeships with both Jean Louis and Edith Head, Mackie has proved an enduringly popular choice for Academy Award clothes. Dale McConathy, in HOLLYWOOD COSTUME—GLAMOUR! GLITTER! ROMANCE!, published in 1976 to complement Diana Vreeland's Metropolitan Museum of Art exhibition, characterized the designer and his then partner Ray Aghayan (with whom he collaborated on such movies as LADY SINGS THE BLUES and FUNNY LADY), as "connoisseurs of Hollywood dressup." Angie Dickinson's vertiginous "suspension" gown (LOT 11), worn to the 1967 Academy Awards, shows Mackie and Aghayan in characteristic form, while Mackie's 1980 ensemble for Sally Field, "a little white suit with a Hawaiian shirt" (LOT 14) which she wore when she won Best Actress for NORMA RAE, illustrates the versatility of a designer usually associated with the arachnoid fantasies he has created for Cher over the years (LOT 5). "People tended to under dress during the seventies," remembers Mackie, "so we wanted to do something unpretentious for a simple California girl." Diane Keaton defined the quirky understatement that characterized the Academy Awards ceremonies throughout the seventies with the homespun layers that she wore when she won Best Actress for ANNIE HALL at the 1978 Academy Awards. For the 1992 awards she honed her signature look, turning to Richard Tyler for a sleek ivory tuxedo pant-suit (LOT 24) that she wore with an overcoat and beret in conscious emulation of the mannish chic of Dietrich and Garbo. "She has her own style," avers Tyler, "she doesn't have to wear a gown if she doesn't want to." Goldie Hawn wore a *trouvaille* from the Paris flea market to the 1975 awards, although Lauren Bacall's classic Fortuny gown (LOT 1), worn to the 1978 Academy Awards (when she presented Oliver Stone with

(top)
Mitzi Gaynor wearing LOT 16,
with Rosemarie and Robert Stack.

(bottom)
Nicole Kidman, Army Archerd
and Tom Cruise at the 1993
Academy Awards. Army Archerd
has greeted stars on the
red carpet for over 40 years.

his screenplay award for MIDNIGHT EXPRESS), represents the apotheosis of vintage dressing.

If Hollywood had been inclined to dress down in the seventies, the following decade reflected the flamboyance of First Lady (and erstwhile MGM contract player) Nancy Reagan and her court, with their dress codes that looked back to the opulent formality of studio dressing. Quintessential eighties designers Emanuel (the husband and wife team of David and Elizabeth Emanuel who created the wedding dress for Lady Diana Spencer's 1981 marriage to the Prince of Wales), are represented by the dress Melanie Griffith wore to the 1988 Academy Awards (LOT 17) that she later had dyed black—a rare example of a dress created for the Oscars® being recycled. And Nolan Miller, the auteur of Joan Collins's coruscating wardrobe for her Alexis Carrington Colby character in the heady television soap opera DYNASTY, is represented by Elizabeth Taylor's full-blown pink taffeta ballgown (LOT 43), worn by the actress to the 1986 Academy Awards. Anjelica Huston reflected a forward-looking simplicity with the one-shouldered emerald crepe dress that she designed herself (LOT 21) and wore when she won Best Supporting Actress for the 1985 PRIZZI'S HONOR, a movie directed by her father, John Huston. 1990 proved a watershed year for Oscar® fashion when Kim Basinger, under the spell of the Artist Formerly Known as Prince, concocted a witty hoop-skirted ivory satin ballgown with a *trompe l'oeil* asymmetrical jacket. The acerbic *Women's Wear Daily* counterpointed an image of Basinger in her exuberant creation with Michelle Pfeiffer in a primly understated Armani, headlining their story THE AGONY AND THE ECSTASY. Giorgio Armani had been wooing Hollywood since his costuming for AMERICAN GIGOLO 1980, and a decade later *WWD* was dubbing the ceremony "The Armani Awards" (LOTS 42, 45). And other designers including Calvin Klein, who dressed Goldie Hawn in 1994 in a bias-cut slip dress (LOT 18) and Sandra Bullock for the 1995 awards (LOT 4), and Randolph Duke for Halston, who dressed Minnie Driver for the 1997 awards (LOT 13) helped to define the new simplicity.

The Basinger debacle was a contributing factor in the ascendancy of the celebrity stylist—the fashion coordinators hired as liasons to help clarify the fashion image of the star, operating very much like the old studio costume departments. With the appearance of supermodels at the Academy Awards (witness Cindy Crawford's 1991 Versace (LOT 7) and Vendela's 1995 Isaac Mizrahi (LOT 47)), and a new generation of actresses like Sharon Stone (LOT 42), Nicole Kidman (LOT 26), Uma Thurman (LOT 46) and Claire Danes (LOT 9) embracing the glamour of old-school Hollywood dressing (at least on Oscar® night), it also signaled a burgeoning relationship between Hollywood stars and international fashion designers.

When Uma Thurman wore her lilac Miuccia Prada dress (designed in consultation with costume designer Barbara Tfank)

(LOT 46) to the 1994 Academy Awards, *Vogue* crowned her "queen of the night" and declared that she "forever demolished the unwritten code for Oscar® attire—understated… or something garishly provocative." The formidable couture technicians Geoffrey Beene and James Galanos used their subtle talents to refined effect in the clothes they created for Glenn Close (Beene, LOT 6), and Jennifer Jones (Galanos, LOT 23). Designer Vera Wang (LOTS 20, 38) blossomed in the public eye through her prominence on Academy Awards nights. Fellow design stars Richard Tyler (LOTS 10, 24, 28, 33, 37) and Mark Badgley and James Mischka (LOTS 30,41), with their talent for translating an archaic idea of glamour into a modern vocabulary, have also emerged as favorite designers to dress the Academy Awards. And nineties haute couture is represented by the master showman Versace (LOTS 2, 7), romantic classicist Valentino (LOTS 26, 42), and the innovative Karl Lagerfeld for Chanel (LOT 12). Lagerfeld's dress, worn by Celine Dion in 1997, with its myriad bugle beads artfully embroidered by Lesage, was a light-handed revisiting of the celebrated souffle dresses created by Jean Louis for Dietrich decades earlier. Kate Winslet's ocean-green satin Givenchy gown and spencer jacket by Alexander McQueen (LOT 51), worn in 1998, and Kristin Scott-Thomas's magnificent Christian Lacroix ballgown from 1997 (LOT 40), reveal both designers, flirtations with nineteenth-century construction techniques and underpinnings.

Of course there is always room for quirky individualism. Madonna's outfit from the same year, which combined pieces by the then 21-year-old Belgian individualist Olivier Theyskens and perennial wild child Jean Paul Gaultier, (concocted with the help of stylist Arianne Phillips) (LOT 32), is testament to an inspired fashionista who in the past has put her imprimatur on outfits by designers as varied as Bob Mackie and John Galliano for Dior.

And who can forget the witty Paco Rabanne-esque dress concocted by Lizzy Gardiner (LOT 15), the winner for Best Costume Design of 1994 (with codesigner Tim Chappel) on THE ADVENTURES OF PRISCILLA, QUEEN OF THE DESERT? Gardiner linked together 171 American Express® gold cards to create her dress, prompting host David Letterman to quip later that her gown had expired.

These outfits and many more, so generously surrendered by designer and star, illustrate the mutual power axis of fashion's foremost creators and movie goddesses that continues to ignite Hollywood's annual night of nights.

Lizzy Gardiner at the 1994 Academy Awards wearing LOT 15.

From Natasha Richardson

I've worked with amfAR since my father died from AIDS in 1991. I don't ever want to see another human being have to suffer the ravages of AIDS; and I don't ever want any loved one or family member to have to watch someone they love die from this cruel disease. I've been through it, and I wouldn't wish it on anyone.

People seem to assume that the worst of the AIDS crisis has passed. In fact, from what I understand, we're on the verge of a major resurgence of HIV infections. Thanks to organizations like amfAR, which fund research programs, there have been serious advances made in terms of suppressive therapy. But these drugs are expensive, and they don't work for everyone forever. What we really have to do is come up with a strategy for a vaccine that is affordable, and accessible to Third World countries—which means more immediate funding for AIDS research.

About two years ago, I heard about the auction of Princess Diana's dresses, and I was struck by the brilliance of that idea. I thought, "What if you gathered together a collection of incredible gowns created for the great women of the film industry for awards ceremonies and gala events?" These dresses, worn once, photographed, are often forgotten in a closet.

Given the huge demand for the Princess's dresses, surely there would be a similar demand—in a totally different way, of course—for historic Hollywood dresses. So I took the idea to amfAR, who then talked to Christie's, at which point we collectively decided to limit the auction to dresses worn to the Oscars®, the most prestigious awards ceremony in the film world.

Our first big hurdle was that the Academy is, understandably, very protective of the word *Oscar®* and the Academy Award logo. But thanks in large part to Mathilde Krim, Ph.D—whose late husband, Arthur B. Krim, was the founder and chairman of Orion, and, prior to that, chairman of United Artists—and the respect for the Krims within the Academy, we were given permission to use the word *Oscar*®, which is unprecedented, and for which we are deeply grateful.

The next task was researching and targeting the dresses we wanted for the auction. In addition to sitting around brainstorming, saying, "Oh, remember so-and-so, she wore a great dress in 1983...," we had to do extensive research. This was a huge collaborative effort between Christie's, us at amfAR, and some enthusiastic fashion stylists. Finally, we came up with a wish list: a very distinguished group of actresses who were included either because they presented, were nominated, or won an award, or because their dresses were particularly spectacular or had great historical or sentimental value.

It's been an interesting process, and thankfully we've had very few outright refusals. Some people, like Uma Thurman and Emma Thompson, responded to my letter by return fax, saying, "Of course you can have it; let me get it for you now." And then there were other people who wanted to help but couldn't. Like Ali McGraw, who lost her entire wardrobe when her house burned down, and Joanne Woodward, who had already donated her dresses to various museums and tried in vain to get them back.

Sometimes it was easy, and I would get enormous satisfaction from an immediate positive response. Other times it seemed like searching for the Holy Grail through an endless sea of publicists, agents, managers, assistants and assistant's assistants.

As most people know, some of the dresses worn to the Oscars® are borrowed from the designers—meaning they aren't the actresses' to give. That's why the involvement of my co-chair, Anna Wintour, the editor-in-chief of *Vogue*, has been so essential. While I have access to the actresses, Anna has access to the designers. Anna and *Vogue* helped with tracking down dresses that we couldn't get via the actresses. I'm also grateful to Anna and her creative team for their impeccable taste in how the dresses are being presented.

This project has turned out to be a huge collaborative effort between people at amfAR, Christie's and *Vogue*, not to mention a host of stylists, designers, publicists, committee members and friends. I would like to thank them all for their invaluable contributions. But most of all, I want to thank the actresses whose generosity has been the most remarkable gesture of all, because these special dresses weren't given lightly. No "star," no matter how big, will ever forget her Oscar® night.

In putting this collection together, our task was in some ways to weave together the history of fashion, movies, and the incredible contributions of so many legendary stars. I don't know how much money we'll raise, but I hope it will be a great deal, as this must be a truly unforgettable auction that I don't think will ever be repeated.

The Dresses

1

THE 1978 ACADEMY AWARDS

Attributed to MARIANO FORTUNY Crimson Pleated Silk Evening Dress

The finely pleated silk column dress with V-shaped bodice is gathered
at the waist with gold cord and dangling tassels. The shoulder, underarm
and tassels are finished with signature Venetian glass beads, which serve
as weights to balance the feather light silk close to the body.

PRESENTER with Jon Voight, Best Screenplay Based on Material from
Another Medium, Oliver Stone, MIDNIGHT EXPRESS

2

Ellen Barkin

THE 1993 ACADEMY AWARDS

GIANNI VERSACE Gold Metal Mesh Evening Dress

The sleeveless fluid ankle-length dress is form-fitted with a
jewel neckline; designed with a rear vent.

ATTENDEE accompanied by Gabriel Byrne

3

Helena Bonham-Carter

DEBORAH MILNER Lavender Silk Taffeta Ball Gown

The dress is designed with a strapless bodice; constructed with a drop waistline and under corset of flesh colored mesh by Mr. Pearl, fitted to a full gathered skirt.

NOMINEE Best Supporting Actress, WINGS OF THE DOVE

4

Sandra Bullock

THE 1995 ACADEMY AWARDS

CALVIN KLEIN Brown Satin-Back Organza Evening Gown

The simple chocolate-brown strapless dress is cut in a princess style;
designed with fitted waist and flared skirt.

PRESENTER Best Sound Effects,
Lon Bender and Per Hallberg, BRAVEHEART

5

Cher

THE 1972 ACADEMY AWARDS

BOB MACKIE Golden Harem Style Ensemble

Designed in a Near Eastern silhouette, from a sheer, lustrous silk fabric
with ornate borders embroidered with golden cord paillettes.

PRESENTER with Sonny Bono, Best Original Song,
"The Morning After," THE POSEIDON ADVENTURE

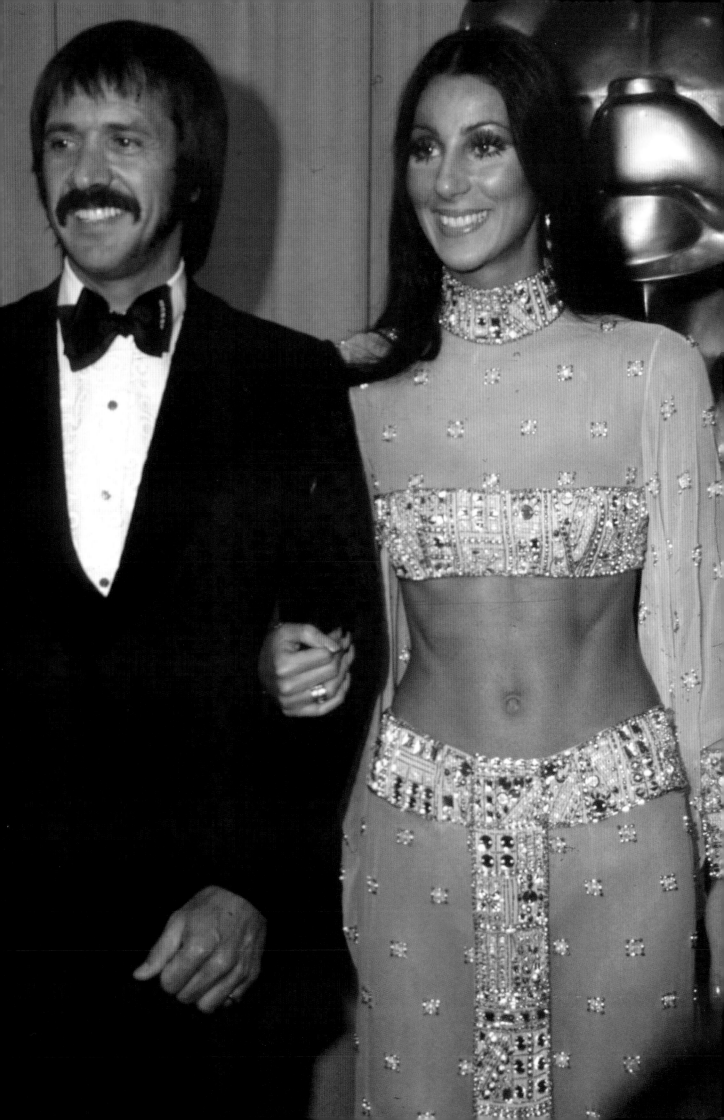

6

Glenn Close

GEOFFREY BEENE Black and Royal Blue Evening Dress

The black column dress with slit center panel design is fitted
with royal blue high pile velvet and eyelash lamé, designed with
a sweetheart shape just below a scooped neckline. Together
with a pair of opera gloves in a matching velvet.

PRESENTER Best Cinematography,
Dean Semler, DANCES WITH WOLVES

7

Cindy Crawford

THE 1990 ACADEMY AWARDS

GIANNI VERSACE COUTURE Scarlet Crepe Evening Dress

The sleeveless bodice is constructed with abstract borders along
a dramatic neckline that mirrors the female figure; designed
with a very exposed back and off-center jeweled closure.

ATTENDEE accompanied by Richard Gere

Eleventh Annual Awards Presentation Dinner
Academy of Motion Picture Arts and Sciences
Biltmore Bowl   Los Angeles
February 23, 1939.

8

Jamie Lee Curtis
THE 1983 ACADEMY AWARDS

JEAN LOUIS for MARLENE DIETRICH
Ivory Bugle Beaded Cocktail Dress

The dress with cap sleeves and a nehru-style collar, gathered
at the waistline with a simple, knee-length skirt.

This dress was designed for Marlene Dietrich and later worn in
THE LADY IS WILLING, 1942. The original design of the dress
was fitted at the waist with a dramatic draped hemline, and long
dolman sleeves.

ATTENDEE accompanied by Michael Riva,
Marlene Dietrich's grandson

9

Claire Danes

NARCISO ROGRIGUEZ for CERRUTI

Aqua Silk-Satin and Cashmere Evening Ensemble

The ankle-length skirt is constructed with triangular panels of aqua silk satin, creating an asymmetrical pattern and fluted hem. Together with a short-sleeve, aqua knit cashmere shell.

PRESENTER Original Song Production Number, *"That Thing You Do"* from THAT THING YOU DO

10

Laura Dern

THE 1993 ACADEMY AWARD

RICHARD TYLER Black Silk Taffeta and Illusion Evening Ensemble

The pleated silk taffeta ball skirt is gathered, constructed with
a high-rise waist and a grand extension of covered buttons along
the full length and train. The sheer illusion body suit is embellished
with a foliate motif appliqué and designed with cap sleeves.

PRESENTER All Scientific and Technical Awards

11

Angie Dickinson

THE 1967 ACADEMY AWARD

RAY AGHAYAN and BOB MACKIE Ivory Crepe Suspension Gown

The sleeveless ivory crepe evening dress is constructed with the skirt suspended below the midriff, held by lattice straps, highlighted with gold scalloped paillettes and "turquoise" beads.

PRESENTER with Gene Kelly, Best Original Score, Elmer Bernstein, THOROUGHLY MODERN MILLIE; Best Scoring of Music— Adaptation or Treatment, Ken Darby and Alfred Newman, CAMELOT

12

Celine Dion

KARL LAGERFELD for CHANEL COUTURE
Black Chiffon Beaded Evening Dress

The halter-style bodice is fashioned with a decollete neckline, embroidered by Lesage with silver paillettes and glass beads. The beading graduates at the midriff to an icicle pattern, then to light, starry highlights. The asymmetrical hem features a high-front vent, finished with a long train. Together with custom shoes by Massaro.

PERFORMER Best Song Nominations, "*Because You Loved Me*,"
UP CLOSE AND PERSONAL and "*I Finally Found You*,"
THE MIRROR HAS TWO FACES (in place of Barbra Streisand)

13

Minnie Driver

THE 1997 ACADEMY AWARDS

RANDOLPH DUKE for HALSTON Ruby Red Jersey Evening Dress

The form fitting bias dress is full-length, designed with
an asymmetrical front drape and plunging back. Together with
a deep red fox stole and matching evening sandals.

NOMINEE Best Supporting Actress, GOOD WILL HUNTING

14

Sally Field

BOB MACKIE

Ivory Silk Crepe Three-Piece Evening Ensemble

The strapless dress is designed with a boned bodice and knee-length wrap skirt. A capped sleeve blouse worn over the bodice is highlighted with sequins and bugle beads in tones of purple, pink and gold, fastening at the waist. Together with a matching ivory jacket.

WINNER Best Actress, NORMA RAE

15

Lizzy Gardiner

THE 1994 ACADEMY AWARDS

LIZZY GARDINER The American Express® Gold Card Dress

An exact replica of the dress constructed of 171 American Express®
Gold Credit Cards, connected entirely by gold-toned links and hooks;
held with chain shoulder straps. Together with a gold organza wrap.

WINNER Best Costume Design with Tim Chappel,
THE ADVENTURES OF PRISCILLA, QUEEN OF THE DESERT

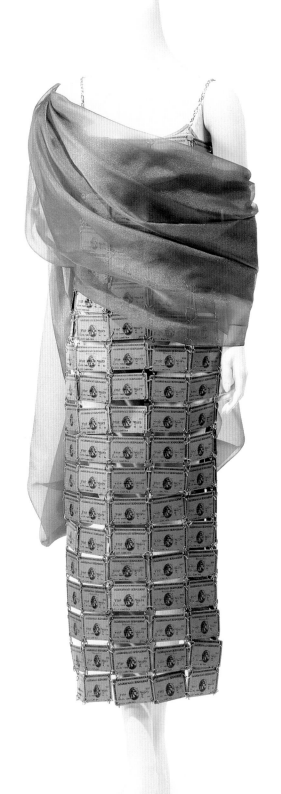

16

Mitzi Gaynor
THE 1966 ACADEMY AWARDS

ARNOLD SCAASI Shell-Pink Silk and Tulle Cocktail Dress

The short, strapless dress is fitted with an empire waist. The tulle
overlay ties at the neck with a matching ribbon, and is embellished
with firework bursts of silver sequins, paillettes and iridescent
shell-shaped baubles, reaching below the hem and dipping
dramatically in the rear. Together with a tulle cape en-suite.

PERFORMER Best Song Nomination,
"Georgy Girl" from GEORGY GIRL

17

Melanie Griffith

EMANUEL Black Silk Ball Gown

The fitted bodice is asymmetrically shirred, creating a soft
V-neckline, held with ruffled off-the-shoulder sleeves and a very
full ball skirt. Together with a black multi-layered crinoline.

This dress was white when worn in 1988, and later
dyed black for Ms. Griffith.

NOMINEE Best Actress, WORKING GIRL

PRESENTER with Don Johnson, Best Supporting Actress,
Brenda Fricker, MY LEFT FOOT

18

Goldie Hawn

THE 1993 ACADEMY AWARDS

CALVIN KLEIN Champagne Colored Full-Length Slip Dress

The simple bias-cut dress is designed in hammered silk-satin,
constructed with slender shoulder straps wrapping around
to a bare back, leading to a slight train.

PRESENTER Best Original Score,
John Williams, SCHINDLER'S LIST

19

Barbara Hershey

THE 1996 ACADEMY AWARDS

GIANNI VERSACE COUTURE
Emerald Stretch Crepe Evening Dress

The strapless column dress is fashioned with a rear flair at the hem.
The unusual shoulder detail of contrasting green sequin-covered
leaves crosses diagonally from front to back.

NOMINEE Best Supporting Actress, PORTRAIT OF A LADY

20

Holly Hunter

VERA WANG Ivory Silk and Illusion Evening Dress

The sleeveless bodice of ivory illusion reaches below the waistline, designed with silk piping at the neckline and arms. The straight skirt is constructed with a soft train; the dress with self-covered button side closure. Worn with a matching ivory, sequined brassiere.

PRESENTER Best Actor, Tom Hanks, FORREST GUMP

21

Anjelica Huston

THE 1985 ACADEMY AWARDS

ANJELICA HUSTON and TZETZI GANEV
Emerald Green Crepe Evening Dress

The asymmetrical empire silhouette dress is designed with a shirred
bodice and single dolman sleeve, leaving the left shoulder bare; the
skirt is draped at the waist and accented with a rear kick-pleat.

WINNER Best Supporting Actress, PRIZZI'S HONOR

22

Anne Jeffreys

THE ACADEMY AWARDS, DATE UNKNOWN

LOUIS ESTEVES Tangerine Silk Faille Evening Dress

The tabard style, sleeveless dress features a halter style bodice
and plunging neckline, surrounded by a strong, geometric motif of
copper bugle beading set with square, rust colored diamantes.
Together with a vibrant orange shawl.

ATTENDEE

Jennifer Jones signing autographs outside Grauman's Chinese Theater before the 1943 Academy Awards.

23

Jennifer Jones
THE 1997 ACADEMY AWARDS

GALANOS Electric Blue and Green Silk Full-Length
Evening Dress and Coat

The long silk dress features all-over foliate pattern of brilliant green
and royal blue, with full overlay of black lace studded with blue
velvet pom-poms. Together with an accompanying coat in blue and
green duchesse silk satin. See illustration page 112.

ATTENDEE 70th Anniversary Reunion of Past Oscar Winners
1943 WINNER Best Actress, THE SONG OF BERNADETTE

24

Diane Keaton

THE 1992 ACADEMY AWARDS

RICHARD TYLER Ivory Gabardine Tuxedo

The three-piece ensemble comprises a suit vest with silk covered buttons, a pair of matching cuffed trousers, a tuxedo jacket with silk-satin peaked lapels and an ivory silk-satin tie.

PRESENTER Best Picture Nominee Film Clip, THE CRYING GAME

25

Sally Kellerman

THE 1970 ACADEMY AWARDS

DON FELD Champagne Cut Velvet Evening Dress

The simple, peasant style, long evening dress is designed with a plunging laced neckline, bordered with bronze and gold bugle beading.

NOMINEE Best Supporting Actress, M * A * S * H

26

Nicole Kidman

THE 1993 ACADEMY AWARDS

VALENTINO Black Silk Velvet Evening Ensemble

The full-length, column dress has a halter style bodice embroidered with jet-beading in a foliate motif. Together with a full-length velvet coat, finished with silk-satin cuffed sleeves.

PRESENTER with Christian Slater, Best Documentary Feature, Alan Raymond and Susan Raymond, I AM A PROMISE: THE CHILDREN OF STANTON ELEMENTARY SCHOOL; Best Documentary Short, Margaret Lazarus and Renner Wunderlich, DEFENDING OUR LIVES

27

Angela Lansbury

THE 1984 ACADEMY AWARDS

PROFILS DU MONDE Ivory Silk Caftan

The caftan is elaborately embroidered in a floral motif with a
variety of crimsons, aquas and greens, interwoven with gold lamé;
constructed with a full-length, covered button front closure. The
pattern recalls "The Tree of Life" from Eastern antiquity.

ACCEPTED ON BEHALF OF Best Supporting Actress,
Dame Peggy Ashcroft, A PASSAGE TO INDIA

28

Cloris Leachman

THE 1997 ACADEMY AWARDS

RICHARD TYLER Olive Silk Taffeta Evening Dress

The shirt-waist dress is fashioned with a tailored bodice, featuring
a banded collar and self-covered button closure from neckline to waist,
with a full ankle-length skirt.

ATTENDEE 70th Anniversary Reunion of Past Oscar Winners
1972 WINNER Best Supporting Actress, THE LAST PICTURE SHOW

29

Janet Leigh
THE 1959 ACADEMY AWARDS

EDITH HEAD Silver Beaded Evening Dress

The pink georgette, ankle-length dress is form fitted,
embroidered overall with silver glass bugle beads, detailed
with stand-up collar and self belt.

PRESENTER with Tony Curtis, Best Screenplay Based
on Material from Another Medium, Neil Peterson,
ROOM AT THE TOP; Best Story and Screenplay Written
Directly for the Screen, Russell Rouse, Clarence Greene,
Stanley Shapiro and Maurice Richlin, PILLOW TALK

30

Jennifer Lopez
THE 1996 ACADEMY AWARDS

BADGLEY MISCHKA Black Chantilly Lace Evening Dress

The long sleeveless asymmetrical dress is constructed with
a lime-colored silk-satin slip under a jet-beaded lace overlay,
designed in a contrasting size floral motif; the scalloped hem
embellished with dense beading.

PRESENTER Best Original Musical or Comedy Score,
Anne Dudley, THE FULL MONTY

31

Shirley MacLaine

THE 1993 ACADEMY AWARDS

ESCADA Black and Royal Blue Formal Ensemble

The suit is comprised of a collarless box jacket, with vest
and trousers; embroidered overall with sequins in a classic
pin-stripe pattern and geometric designs.

PRESENTER Best Sound, Gary Summers, Gary Rydstrom,
Shawn Murphy and Ron Judkins, JURASSIC PARK

32

Madonna

THE 1997 ACADEMY AWARDS

OLIVIER THEYSKENS and JEAN PAUL GAULTIER
Black Silk Faille and Dove-Gray Tulle Evening Ensemble

The black silk robe redingote, designed by Oliver Theyskens
features a sweeping train adorned with chantilly lace;
opening below the waist to reveal a dove-gray ball skirt,
of multi-layered tulle by Gaultier.

PRESENTER Best Original Song,
"*My Heart Will Go On*" from TITANIC

33

Frances McDormand

THE 1996 ACADEMY AWARDS

RICHARD TYLER Royal Blue Duchesse Silk Satin Evening Dress

The empire-style bodice is designed with a square halter
neckline and slender straps that criss-cross over the open back.
The straight skirt is highlighted with rear pleating. Together
with a matching stole of alternating black and royal-blue panels.

WINNER Best Actress, FARGO

34

Bette Midler

THE 1996 ACADEMY AWARDS

PAMELA DENNIS Navy Blue Silk Jersey Evening Dress

The classic short sleeve column dress is designed with
a square neckline, embellished with navy diamantés and
a cascading beaded floral motif.

PRESENTER with Diane Keaton and Goldie Hawn,
Best Original Song, Sir Andrew Lloyd Webber and
Tim Rice, "*You Must Love Me*" from EVITA

35

Kathleen Quinlan

PAMELA BARISH Forest Green Cut Velvet Evening Dress

The column dress is fashioned with a dramatic draped back and slightly flared hem, designed in cut velvet in a floral motif.

NOMINEE Best Supporting Actress, APOLLO 13

36

Vanessa Redgrave

THE 1992 ACADEMY AWARDS

BRUCE OLDFIELD Black Gabardine Evening Suit

The bodice of this single-breasted evening jacket is constructed
of vertical panels sewn together, solid until the hip, then separating,
creating a long fringe finished in points. Together with a matching
pair of black gabardine trousers.

NOMINEE Best Supporting Actress, HOWARDS END

37

Julia Roberts

RICHARD TYLER Black Silk-Crepe Evening Dress

The full length black dress, fashioned after a man's tail coat, of structured form, highlighted with a funnel neckline, loop and button front closure. The skirt is designed with four dramatic vents and under-panels of silk chiffon, the hem embellished with zigzag bugle beading.

NOMINEE Best Actress, PRETTY WOMAN

38

Meg Ryan
THE 1997 ACADEMY AWARDS

VERA WANG Navy Blue Silk Jersey Evening Dress

The long-sleeved, full-length sheath dress is fashioned with a flared
hem, the triangular neckline and sleeves finished with soft points.

PRESENTER Best Art Direction,
Peter Lamont and Michael Ford, TITANIC

39

Susan Sarandon
THE 1997 ACADEMY AWARDS

DOLCE & GABBANA Black Stretch Tulle Gala Ensemble

The fitted bodice is constructed with a corselet foundation, overlaid
with black shirred stretch tulle. The transparent skirt gathers to a
train, held with fine silk flowers in tones of lavender, fawn and gold.
Together with underpinning.

PRESENTER Introduction of 70th Anniversary
Reunion of past Oscar Winners

1995 WINNER Best Actress, DEAD MAN WALKING

40

Kristin Scott-Thomas
THE 1996 ACADEMY AWARDS

CHRISTIAN LACROIX COUTURE
Black Gazar, Organza and Gauze Evening Dress

The long black gazar, organza and gauze dress with draped
décolleté and pleated flap bustle.

NOMINEE Best Actress, THE ENGLISH PATIENT
PRESENTER with Jack Valenti, Best Foreign Language Film, KOLYA

41

Elizabeth Shue

THE 1997 ACADEMY AWARDS

BADGLEY MISCHKA Butterscotch Printed Silk Evening Dress

The sleeveless bodice is quilted with matching metallic cord and beading, the long straight skirt designed in an elaborate motif.

PRESENTER Best Costume Design, Deborah L. Scott, TITANIC

42

Sharon Stone

THE 1995 ACADEMY AWARDS

GIORGIO ARMANI, VALENTINO and GAP

The full-length, black silk-crepe trumpet skirt, lined in silk
charmeuse is designed by Valentino. Accompanied by a full-length
black silk velvet dressmaker's coat by Giorgio Armani. Together
with a black stretch-cotton GAP t-shirt.

NOMINEE Best Actress, CASINO
PRESENTER with Quincy Jones, Best Dramatic Score, Louis
Enrique Bacalor, IL POSTINO; Best Comedy Score, Mencken and
Schwartz, POCAHONTAS.

43

Meryl Streep

THE 1979 ACADEMY AWARDS

PAULINE TRIGÈRE Ivory Evening Ensemble

The strapless, full-length dress is designed with a fitted bodice highlighted with jewel-tone diamantés. Together with an ivory evening
jacket, constructed with puffed sleeves and jewel toned buttons.

WINNER Best Supporting Actress, KRAMER VS. KRAMER

44

Elizabeth Taylor
THE 1986 ACADEMY AWARDS

NOLAN MILLER Pink Silk Taffeta Evening Dress

The corset formed bodice is highlighted with a shirred bustline gigot
style, three-quarter length sleeves. The waist and cuffs are finished with
a point, the back of the skirt features a sunburst pleat between full-
length ruffles, adorned with pink silk stemmed roses at the waistline.

PRESENTER Best Director, Oliver Stone, PLATOON

45

Emma Thompson

THE 1995 ACADEMY AWARDS

GIORGIO ARMANI

Ivory Silk Georgette and Silk Jersey Evening Ensemble

The short jacket of silk georgette is embellished with seed beads and sequins, bordered in silk jersey. The full-length, silk-crepe wrap skirt is designed with an off-center, single button closure and rounded hem.

WINNER Best Screenplay Based on Previously Published Material, SENSE AND SENSIBILITY

NOMINEE Best Actress, SENSE AND SENSIBILITY

46

Uma Thurman

PRADA Lavender Silk Chiffon Evening Dress

The full-length sleeveless dress is designed in a classic princess
style silhouette, constructed with a cinched midriff flaring into a
flowing skirt with chiffon overlay, embellished with iridescent
paillettes. Together with a cream silk-organza wrap, lavender satin
handbag and shoes.

NOMINEE Best Supporting Actress, PULP FICTION

PRESENTER Best Makeup, Rick Baker, Ve neill, Yolanda Toussieng,
ED WOOD

47

ISAAC MIZRAHI Shocking Pink Georgette Evening Dress

The full-length fitted dress is designed with flowing skirt
and held with matching silk satin ribbon halter, embroidered
overall with iridescent sequins.

ATTENDEE

48

Emily Watson

THE 1996 ACADEMY AWARDS

AMANDA WAKELY Silver-Gray Silk Chiffon Evening Dress

The slip dress features thin shoulder straps and a V-neckline,
with a simple leaf motif on the bodice. The skirt is asymmetrically
tiered and draped with cascading fabric.

NOMINEE Best Supporting Actress, BREAKING THE WAVES

49

Raquel Welch

THE 1978 ACADEMY AWARDS

LORIS AZZARO Royal Blue Sequined Catsuit

The form-fitting one piece catsuit is embroidered overall in shimmering sequins, designed with a V-neckline and thin shoulder straps.

PRESENTER with Dean Martin, Best Original Score, Joe Renzetti, THE BUDDY HOLLY STORY

50

Rita Wilson

THE 1994 ACADEMY AWARDS

HERVÉ LEGER Black Jersey Evening Dress

The body-hugging sleeveless dress is constructed from
horizontally worked ribbons of black stretch jersey.
The bodice is highlighted with clustered, simulated pearl
beading, diamantés on the bust and open back.

ATTENDEE accompanied by husband Tom Hanks
(WINNER Best Actor, FORREST GUMP)

51

Kate Winslet

THE 1997 ACADEMY AWARDS

ALEXANDER MCQUEEN for GIVENCHY Forest Green Silk Crepe
Marocain and Duchesse Silk Satin Evening Ensemble

The full-length evening dress of rich green silk crepe marocain and
matching bolero of duchesse silk satin are both hand-embroidered by
Hurel with silk thread and crystal beads in a weeping willow branch
and dragonfly motif.

NOMINEE Best Supporting Actress, TITANIC

52

Lili Zanuck

THE 1989 ACADEMY AWARDS

LORIS AZZARO Black Georgette Evening Dress

The long tunic bodice is intricately draped and gathered, with a flowing skirt.

WINNER Best Producer, with husband Richard D. Zanuck, DRIVING MISS DAISY

53

Elizabeth Taylor

THE 1969 ACADEMY AWARDS

EDITH HEAD Periwinkle Blue and Violet Faille
Crepe Evening Dress

A sleeveless dress with fitted bodice and décolleté neckline.
The full skirt with an asymmetrical double flounce of blue and
violet fabric descending and cascading from the waistline,
revealing a vibrant violet petticoat.

PRESENTER Best Picture, MIDNIGHT COWBOY

54

Mystery Dress

INDEX

CELEBRITY INDEX

DESIGNER INDEX

amfAR

AIDS RESEARCH

AMERICAN FOUNDATION FOR AIDS RESEARCH

The **American Foundation for AIDS Research** (amfAR) is the nation's leading nonprofit organization dedicated to the support of HIV/AIDS research. Seeking prevention methods (including a vaccine), improved treatments, and ultimately a cure, amfAR-funded research is contributing significantly to the lives of people with HIV/AIDS and to the global effort to arrest the epidemic.

Funded by private philanthropic contributions, amfAR has invested nearly $150 million in support for its programs since 1985, primarily through grants awarded to 1,745 research teams. In fact, more than 78% of all funds received by amfAR over the past fourteen years has been invested in its research programs. These programs fund innovative, scientifically sound projects that may carry a level of risk higher than projects supported by most traditional grant makers. A project's selection—following a peer review by highly qualified professionals who volunteer their advisory services—is based on promise, relevance, and scientific merit.

amfAR's basic research program seeks the knowledge needed to understand HIV and its disease-causing properties so that strategies can be devised to control and prevent HIV infection. In the past, grants and scholar-training awards have supported

- pioneering research leading to the use of zidovudine (AZT) to prevent HIV transmission from mother to newborn;
- early HIV protease research that was critical to the development of protease inhibitors;
- studies that led to the discovery of the CCR5 co-receptor, a cellular molecule required (by most strains of HIV) for the infection and destruction of crucial immune cells;
- early research leading to the first three-dimensional images showing the structure of gp120, a viral protein that enables HIV to latch on to the cell it subsequently infects: knowledge of gp120's structure is a critical piece of information required for the design of HIV vaccines;
- innovative strategies for the restoration of functioning immune systems in patients with HIV disease who have responded to highly active anti-retroviral therapy (HAART);
- creative research to achieve immunization through the use of "naked DNA:" This approach is now being applied to the search for vaccination against HIV;
- investigations that resulted in the official classification of invasive cervical cancer as an AIDS-defining condition in HIV-positive women;
- early studies on the use of gene therapy to suppress HIV, including the first clinical study of intracellular immunization; and
- surveys that established certain sexually transmitted diseases (STDs), other than HIV, as co-factors in HIV transmission, and led to the worldwide effort to curb the spread of HIV by preventing or treating these STDs.

amfAR funded the first studies on ethics in AIDS research, prevention, and care—studies that led to the development of public policies to protect the confidentiality of medical information and the privacy of people with HIV/AIDS.

amfAR initiated the pioneering "care" concept and facilitated the enactment of the Ryan White CARE Act of 1990 by providing staff assistance to the Senate Committee on Labor and Human Resources. The CARE Act, which includes the AIDS Drug Assistance Program, ensures that cities and states nationwide have access to emergency relief for the care and treatment of people with HIV/AIDS.

amfAR advocated and facilitated enactment of (1) the HOPE Act of 1988, the first comprehensive federal law to combat AIDS; (2) the Americans with Disabilities Act of 1990, which includes protection for people infected or perceived to be infected with HIV; and (3) the National Institutes of Health (NIH) Revitalization Act of 1993, which strengthened the NIH's Office of AIDS Research.

amfAR established (by direct measurements of seroconversion rates) that "needle exchange" reduces the rate of HIV transmission among IV-drug users without increasing the use of illicit drugs.

Through its sponsorship of community forums, physician-update seminars, and continuing-medical-education conferences, amfAR provides up-to-date treatment information to lay audiences, physicians, and caregivers.

AIDS research has already achieved results that are lengthening and improving the lives of many people with HIV disease. But as the HIV/AIDS epidemic continues to spread throughout the world, every dollar contributed to research becomes even more important.

The mission of the American Foundation for AIDS Research is to prevent HIV infection and the disease and death associated with it and to protect the human rights of all people threatened by the epidemic of HIV/AIDS.

BOARD MEMBERS

ACKNOWLEDGMENTS

As with any project large and complex, "Unforgettable: Fashion of the Oscars®" represents the efforts of many people working in close collaboration over many months.

We must, of course, begin with Natasha Richardson who first presented her brilliant idea to us in the middle of our annual event in Cannes. We thank her for her insight, creativity, hard work, and not least, for her generosity in bringing yet another project to amfAR. She has been—and continues to be—a much loved and valued friend in the battle against AIDS.

The project was immediately presented to Mathilde Krim and Mouna Ayoub, both of whom embraced the idea and presciently predicted its extraordinary success. Their encouragement, along with that of Elizabeth Taylor, was invaluable in keeping this effort moving forward. Their constant work on the amfAR board remains, as ever, the inspiration for all our efforts each and every day.

Thanks are also due to Francois Curiel and Meredith Etherington-Smith of Christie's for their early encouragement and support.

This project would never have happened without the invaluable advice of Bruce Davis of the Academy of Motion Picture Arts and Sciences. We also are deeply grateful for the Academy's support and blessing in allowing us to use the name "Oscar®" in conjunction with this effort. Access to the Academy library allowed us not just to verify that the dresses are truly "Oscar® dresses" but to ensure that this catalog represented the best—and the most memorable— photographic images of Oscar® nights past. Though the list is long we must thank all the librarians, archivists, and pages of Special Collections at the Margaret Herrick Library in Beverly Hills: Eddie Baker, Norm Brennan, Ed Carter, Robert Cushman, Lisa Epstein, Steve Garland, Sue Guldin, Nicole Harvey, Mona Huntzing, Kristine Krueger, Andrea Livingston, Nancy Lucchese, David Marsh, Robert Rioux, Faye Thompson, Jonathan Wahl, and Libby Worton. We could not have done this project without them.

Many, many people contributed to the acquisitions that are illustrated in this catalog. We appreciate the input, ideas, and contributions of all our fashion experts: Philip Bloch, Patty Fox, Maury Hopson, Jane Ross, L'Wren Scott, and Laurence Taylor all provided critical assistance in helping us "curate" this unbelievable collection. Similarly, our most sincere thanks are due to John Hayles of MCA, Sandy Mason of American Express®, Wanda McDaniel of Giorgio Armani, Nolan Miller, Elizabeth Reid of Valentino, Elizabeth Rogers of Calvin Klein, Lee Sippola of Richard Tyler, Bill Sutton, and Rita Watnick of Lily et Cie for sharing with us their recollections, and their love, of beautiful clothes.

The contributions of other special friends have greatly enriched our work on the project. As always, we acknowledge the indispensible support of Continental Airlines, whose sponsorship allowed the whole staff to travel gratis on this project. We also owe thanks to the staff, especially Cassandra, at the Mondrian Hotel who were so generous and hospitable. They made business trips and meetings a pleasure. Our love and thanks to Jose Eber for asking his friends to be part of this: special thanks also to all of his terrific staff, but most particularly to Morgan McNally for her tireless efforts on our behalf. We are indebted to Tim Mendelson for his introductions, input, energy and enthusiasm; most of all, however, we thank him for helping us track down that elusive lot: Elizabeth Taylor's 1969 Edith Head!

Anna Wintour is due untold thanks for her critical participation in the project. In addition to *Vogue* magazine's underwriting of the entire event, her insight, style, and extraordinary taste have helped shape "Unforgettable" in every way: it is a far better project for her creative contribution. We also appreciate the dedicated work of her staff, in particular Hamish Bowles, Anne Buford, Charles Churchward, Patrick O'Connell and Stephanie B. Winston.

Many in the world of fashion were generous in their support of this project. We are most grateful for the personal contributions of Mark Badgeley and James Mischka, Anne Fahey of Chanel, Lizzie Gardiner, Jean Paul Gaultier, Christian Lacroix, Alexander McQueen, Bruce Oldfield, Richard Tyler, and Valentino.

We also owe thanks to Simon Doonan and Barneys New York for the major contribution of exhibition design and mannequins. To Wayne Edelman at Meurice Garment Care for the unbelievable donation of dry cleaning for the entire project. The styling by Christopher Fey has made this catalog truly unforgetttable.

We owe everything to the actresses, who generously, selflessly, opened their hearts and their closets to amfAR and its cause. Their gifts will live on, not just on the pages of this catalog, but in the minds of all of us at amfAR. We are proud that the greatest actresses in Hollywood remain steadfastly committed to finding a vaccine and a cure for AIDS.

Also, we must thank those frequently unsung, but always helpful publicists whose efforts made it possible for us to assemble such an extraordinary collection in such a short amount of time. Our thanks go to Kelly Bush of IDPR; Katie

Ogan and Evelyn Dallal of Ogan Dallal; Cindi Berger, Allen Eichorn, Robert Garlock, and Heidi Schaeffer of PMK; and Liz Rosenberg of Warner Brothers Records. No project could have had better advocates and ambassadors.

Finally, our profound thanks go to all those people who worked daily on this project to make it the outstanding success that it is. At Christie's, we salute Patricia Hambrecht, the indomitable Susy Korb, and their outstanding staff. We know that without the daily efforts of the Christie's team this project would have been far inferior. Their exacting standards and thoughtful guidance ensured the overall excellence of all aspects of the project. At amfAR, too, the project benefitted from the constant attention of the "Unforgettable" dream team. We thank Diane Boehm, who directed the project, for her goodspirited and generous attention to each and every aspect of the acquisition process; Mindy Alberman, for the meticulous attention to every detail of the research phase, which unearthed the extraordinary images that are featured in the catalog; Delphine Hirsh, for her always energetic contributions to all aspects of "Unforgettable"; Stephanie Landess Jeffrey, for her expertise in cataloguing the donations; and Rita White, for her always cheerful and unflagging commitment to all amfAR projects. Finally, we thank Jerome J. Radwin, for once more having faith in an idea, and allowing us to run with it.

Scott Campbell and Sally Morrison, amfAR

EACH DRESS HAS KINDLY BEEN DONATED BY THE FOLLOWING:

1   Lauren Bacall
2   Ellen Barkin
3   Helena Bonham-Carter
4   Sandra Bullock
5   Cher
6   Glenn Close
7   Cindy Crawford
8   Jamie Lee Curtis
    and The Riva Family
9   Claire Danes
10 Laura Dern
11 Angie Dickinson
12 Chanel Couture
13 Minnie Driver
14 Sally Field
15 Lizzy Gardiner
    and American Express®
16 Mr. and Mrs. Spencer Brown,
    Rita Watnick
    and Michael Stoyla (Lily et Cie)

17 Melanie Griffith
18 Goldie Hawn
19 Barbara Hershey
20 Holly Hunter
21 Anjelica Huston
22 Anne Jeffreys
23 Jennifer Jones
24 Diane Keaton
25 Sally Kellerman
26 Valentino
27 Angela Lansbury
28 Richard Tyler
29 Janet Leigh
30 Badgley Mischka
31 Shirley MacLaine
32 Madonna
33 Frances McDormand
34 Bette Midler
35 Kathleen Quinlan
36 Vanessa Redgrave
    and Bruce Oldfield

37 Julia Roberts
38 Meg Ryan
39 Susan Sarandon
40 Christian Lacroix
41 Elizabeth Shue
42 Sharon Stone
43 Meryl Streep
44 Elizabeth Taylor
45 Emma Thompson
46 Uma Thurman
47 William F. Sutton
48 Emily Watson
49 Raquel Welch
50 Hervé Leger
51 Kate Winslet
52 Lili Zanuck
53 Elizabeth Taylor
54 To be announced

PHOTOGRAPHY CREDITS

Courtesy of the Academy of Motion Picture Arts and Sciences

"Academy Award (s)" and "Oscar (s)" are registered trademarks and service marks of the Academy of Motion Picture Arts and Sciences. The Award of Merit statuette ("Oscar") is a copyrighted work of art, and is also an A.M.P.A.S. trademark and service mark.

© Copyright Academy of Motion Picture Arts and Sciences

The following images are reprinted with kind permission of the Academy of Motion Picture Arts and Sciences Pages: Cover, Endpages, 8, 10, 11, 12, 13, 14, 20, 22, 24, 26, 30, 33, 34-35, 36, 39, 40, 42, 44, 47, 48-49, 51, 52, 54, 56, 58, 60, 62, 65, 66-67, 70, 72, 75, 77, 78, 80, 82, 84, 85-86, 90, 93, 95, 96, 98, 100, 101, 102, 108, 110, 111-112, 116, 118, 121, 122, 124, 126-127, 128, 131, 132, 135, 137

Courtesy of Ron Galella   Page: 29

Courtesy of Globe Photos   Pages: 88, 114, 107

Courtesy of Pamela Hansen Page: 17

Courtesy of Anne Jeffreys   Page: 68

Dress photography by Christie's in-house photographer: David Schlegel

CHRISTIE'S

SPECIALISTS AND SERVICES FOR THIS SALE

For assistance and further information about this sale, please contact the following:

Stacey Sayer
Auction Coordinator

Brenda Little
Auction Administrator

Tel   (212) 702 3709
Fax   (212) 446 9566

General Information
For general client assistance:

Tel   (212) 546 1010

For 24-hour recorded information on current sales and exhibitions:

Tel   (212) 371 5438

Sales Results
Clients with "touch-tone" telephones can directly access our sales results.

New York Sales Results:
Tel   (212) 452 4100

London Sales Results:
Tel   (44 171) 627 2707

Absentee and Telephone Bids
For arrangement of bids for those who cannot attend the sale:

Barbara Strongin
Tel   (212) 546 1127
Fax   (212) 832 2216

Auction Tickets
To request tickets to the auction:

Tel   (212) 546 5859
Fax   (212) 446 9566

Payment
For buyer assistance on terms of payment:

Vin Bissoondial
Tel   (212) 546 1040

Jennifer Galkoski
Pam Mackin
Kathrine Grossmann
Tel   (212) 546 1059
Fax   (212) 317 2439

or method of payment:

Lynne Gardner
Tel   (212) 546 1124
Fax   (212) 759 7204

Shipping
For information on shipping of purchased property:

Chantal Lakatos
Tel   (212) 546 1113
Fax   (212) 980 8195

Internet Access
For information about Christie's services and forthcoming sales:

on-line: www.christies.com

Client Advisory Service
Professional advice for the private collector:

Tel   (212) 546 1036
Fax   (212) 750 1537

Kate Gubelman
Head of Department
Tel   (212) 546 1122

Kathy Kermian
Head of Department
Tel   (212) 546 1126

Heidi Kucker
Senior Director
Tel   (212) 546 1031

Kim Solow
Tel   (212) 702 2627

Jennifer Kaplan
Sharon Kim
Elizabeth Sarnoff
Tel   (212) 546 1074

Gabriela Lobo
Department Administrator
Tel   (212) 546 1021

Maria Los
Department Administrator
Tel   (212) 546 1036

Mirja Spooner
Department Administrator
Tel   (212) 546 5824

Ken C.Y. Yeh
Chinese Client Liaison
Tel   (212) 546 5898

Shoko Suzuki
Japanese Client Liaison
Tel   (212) 546 5892

Julie Kim
Korean Client Liaison
Tel   (212) 546 5840

Catalogue Subscriptions
To subscribe to Christie's catalogues:

Tel   (800) 395 6300
Fax   (800) 395 5600

Outside the U.S. and Canada:
Tel   (718) 784 1480
Fax   (718) 786 0941

Christie's Auction Search Service: Lot Finder™
For clients looking for something specific, we have an auction search service that can notify you of items of interest to you in Christie's worldwide sales. If you would like to register with this service, please telephone:

New York (212) 546 5815
London (44 171) 389 2963

SPECIAL SALE INFORMATION

SALES TAX INFORMATION

Christie's is offering all lots in this catalogue as agent for an organization holding a State of New York Exempt Organization Certificate. Accordingly, no sales tax is due on the purchase price of the lots if the property is picked up or delivered in the State of New York. However, a sales or use tax is due from the buyer if any such lot is shipped to New Jersey or Connecticut or any of the following states where Christie's maintains offices: Alabama, California, Florida, Illinois, Massachusetts, Pennsylvania, Rhode Island, Texas and Washington D.C.

CHARITABLE STATUS

Although a portion of sale proceeds of any lot and profits from the catalogue will benefit an American charity, any purchaser who is a U.S. taxpayer may not deduct any portion of the purchase price of any lot or the cost of the catalogue as a charitable donation within the meaning of Section 170 of the Internal Revenue Code.

ESTIMATE PRICES AND RESERVES

No estimates have been printed in this catalogue. As a guideline only, a minimum bid of US$2,000 per lot is recommended.

Each lot is being offered for sale without reserve.

This sale is a charity sale conducted by Christie's on a not-for-profit basis. The American Foundation for Aids Research is to benefit.

BUYERS PREMIUM

Buyers are reminded that the purchase price will be the sum of the final bid price plus the buyer's premium, which is generally 15% of the final bid price up to and including $50,000 and 10% of the amount above $50,000.

NEW BUYERS

If you are a new client, or if you have not made a recent purchase at Christie's, you may be asked to supply a bank reference when you register. To avoid any delay in the release of your purchases, you may wish to prearrange check or credit approval. If so, please contact Christie's Credit Department at (212) 546 1040 or by fax at (212) 754 2390.

CONDITION REPORTS

You are encouraged to request Condition Reports, as the garments may not be physically examined or tried on during the view.

To request a Condition Report please contact

Brenda Little
Tel   (212) 702 3709
Fax   (212) 446 9566

STORAGE

All purchases must be collected not later than 5 p.m. of the next business day after the sale. After five business days, an administration fee of $30 and a storage fee of $3 per day, per lot will be charged.

AUCTION PRACTICE AT CHRISTIE'S

Christie's History

Christie's, the world's oldest fine art auctioneers, held its first auction in London on December 5, 1766.

In 1977 Christie's opened its first saleroom in America at 502 Park Avenue, followed in 1979 by Christie's East at 219 East 67th Street. In May 1997 Christie's launched a third United States saleroom—Christie's Los Angeles, 360 North Camden Drive, Beverly Hills. Today the firm is a major international company with 119 offices in 41 countries. Christie's holds sales in Britain, the United States, Australia, Hong Kong, Greece, Italy, Monaco, the Netherlands, Singapore and Switzerland. This worldwide network of salerooms enables sellers to take advantage of seasonal selling peaks, national tastes and collecting habits, and fluctuating currency exchange rates.

Over the centuries, Christie's has conducted many of the most important sales ever held. In the late 18th century the firm negotiated the sale of Sir Robert Walpole's collection to Catherine the Great who immediately installed the works in the Hermitage where many of them can be seen today. In 1794 Christie's held a five-day sale of the contents of Sir Joshua Reynolds's studio, and sold Madame du Barry's jewels in 1795, the year she was guillotined. In 1848, in a sale lasting 40 days, the firm sold the collection of the Duke of Buckingham at Stowe House.

In more recent years, Christie's in America has sold major Impressionist, Modern and Contemporary paintings from numerous renowned collections such as those of Henry Ford II, Paul Mellon, Baron Lambert, the Tremaines, Robert B. Mayer, John and Frances L. Loeb and Victor and Sally Ganz; and from distinguished

Hollywood collections such as those of William and Edith Mayer Goetz, Hal B. Wallis and Billy Wilder. Other pre-eminent sales held in America include the Codex Hammer which sold for $30,800,000 – the most expensive work other than a painting ever sold, the Nicholas Brown desk and bookcase which sold for $12,100,000 – the record for American furniture, the jewels of Florence Gould and Caroline Ryan Foulke, the Estelle Doheny Library (which included Volume I of the Gutenberg Bible, sold for $5,390,000, a world record price for a printed book), and many important sales of furniture, Asian arts, porcelain, rugs, silver, stamps, wine and automobiles. In 1990, Christie's set world records for both paintings and furniture, when van Gogh's Portrait of Dr. Gachet sold for $82,500,000 in New York and the Badminton Cabinet reached $15,200,000 in London.

Christie's welcomes you to our viewing galleries and salerooms. Our specialists and client service staff will be pleased to help you with any aspect of buying or selling at auction.

The Buyer

USING THIS CATALOGUE

Estimate Prices and Reserves
No estimates have been printed in this catalogue. *As a guideline only, a minimum bid of U.S. $2,000 per lot is recommended.*

Each lot is being offered for sale without reserve.

This sale is a charity sale conducted by Christie's on a not-for-profit basis. The American Foundation for Aids Research is to benefit.

Conditions of Sale and Limited Warranty
If you wish to bid in a sale, we encourage you to read the **Conditions of Sale** and **Limited Warranty** which appear on the pages immediately following. The **Conditions of Sale** outline the terms governing the purchase of all property sold at auction. The **Limited Warranty** specifies the terms and conditions upon which Christie's guarantees the authenticity of property offered for sale.

Buyer's Premium and Sales Tax
Buyers are reminded that the purchase price will be the sum of the final bid price plus the buyer's premium, which is generally 15% of the final bid price up to and including $50,000 and 10% of the amount above $50,000.

In addition to the purchase price, buyers are required to pay any sales or use tax which may be due. These charges are explained in detail under "Christie's Charges and Sales Tax" towards the end of this catalogue.

BEFORE THE AUCTION

Pre-sale viewings for all our auctions are open to the public and may be attended at no charge. All property to be auctioned is usually on view for several days prior to the sale. You are encouraged to examine lots thoroughly and to request condition reports (see below). Christie's specialists and customer service staff are available to give advice at all viewings or by appointment.

Hours of Business
Christie's Park Avenue galleries and Christie's East are open from 10 a.m. to 5 p.m. on weekdays. During the auction season there is frequent

weekend viewing from 10 a.m. to 5 p.m. on Saturdays and varying afternoon hours on Sundays. The viewing schedule for each sale is published in the front of the auction catalogue.

Condition Reports

If you would like additional information on a particular lot or cannot come to the viewing, Christie's will be pleased to provide upon request a condition report. Please contact the department in charge of the sale.

We remind prospective buyers that descriptions of property are not warranties and that each lot is sold "as is" in accordance with the terms of the **Limited Warranty**. Condition reports are provided as a service to interested clients, but the information furnished does not negate or modify the **Limited Warranty**. Neither Christie's nor the consignor makes any express or implied warranty or representation as to the condition of any lot offered for sale, and no statement made at any time, whether oral or written, shall constitute such a warranty or representation.

Registration

Owing to the anticipated interest in the sale, admission will be limited to catalogue purchase and ticket request only. For a sale ticket please call (212) 546 5859. If you are a new client, or if you have not made a recent purchase at Christie's, you may be asked to supply a bank reference when you register. To avoid any delay in the release of your purchases, you may wish to prearrange check or credit approval. If so, please contact Christie's Credit Department at (212) 546 1040 or by fax at (212) 754 2390.

THE AUCTION

See preceding note under "Registration" regarding admission to the sale.

Bidding

Property is auctioned in consecutive numerical order, as it appears in the catalogue. The lot being offered is usually shown at the front of the saleroom or is illustrated on a slide screen. The auctioneer will accept bids from those present in the saleroom or absentee bidders participating by telephone or by written bid left with Christie's in advance of the auction. The auctioneer may also execute bids on behalf of the consignor to protect the reserve, either by placing consecutive bids up to the amount of the reserve or by entering bids in response to saleroom, telephone or absentee bids. Under no circumstances will the auctioneer place any bid on behalf of the consignor at or above the reserve. Nor will the auctioneer specifically identify bids placed on behalf of the consignor to protect the reserve.

Bidding Increments

Bidding generally opens below the low estimate and advances in the following increments:

$500 to $1,000	by $50
$1,000 to $2,000	by $100
$2,000 to $3,000	by $200
$3,000 to $5,000	by $200 or $200-500-800
$5,000 to $10,000	by $500
$10,000 to $20,000	by $1,000
$20,000 to $30,000	by $2,000
$30,000 to $50,000	by $2,000 or $2000-5000-8000
$50,000 to $100,000	by $5,000
$100,000 to $200,000	by $10,000
$200,000 up	Auctioneer's discretion

Occasionally the auctioneer may vary the increments during the course of the auction at his or her discretion.

Currency Conversion

Christie's may, as a convenience to bidders, use a currency conversion board during the auction to display the amounts being bid converted into several foreign currencies. These converted amounts are approximations only and may not represent the exact exchange rate at any given time.

Absentee Bids

If you cannot attend an auction, you may bid in other ways. The most common is the absentee bid, sometimes called an "order bid." Absentee bids are written instructions from you directing Christie's to bid for you on one or more lots up to a maximum amount you specify for each lot. Christie's staff will attempt execute your absentee bid at the lowest possible price taking into account the reserve price and other bids. There is no charge for this service. If identical bids are left by two or more parties, the first bid received by Christie's will take preference. The auctioneer may execute bids for absentee bidders directly from the podium, clearly identifying these as order bids. Absentee Bid Forms are available in the back of every auction catalogue and also may be obtained at any Christie's location.

While Christie's will make every effort to execute absentee bids, the service is offered as an accommodation to our customers, and Christie's is not liable for any failures to execute bids, errors or omissions in their execution.

Telephone Bids

Christie's will also execute your bids if you cannot come to the auction and wish to participate by telephone. Arrangements should be confirmed at least one day in advance of the sale with Christie's Bid Department at (212) 546 1127. Christie's staff will execute telephone bids from designated areas in the saleroom. This service is also free of charge.

While Christie's will make every effort to execute telephone bids, the service is offered as an accommodation to our customers, and Christie's is not liable for any failures to execute bids, errors or omissions in their execution.

Successful Bids

The fall of the auctioneer's hammer indicates the final bid. Christie's will record the paddle number of the buyer. If your saleroom or absentee bid is successful, you will be notified immediately after the sale by mailed invoice. If you are unsuccessful, Christie's Bid Department will notify you by letter.

Unsold Lots

If a lot does not reach the reserve, it is bought-in. In other words, it remains unsold and is returned to the consignor. When the auctioneer hammers down a lot that fails to sell, he will so indicate by announcing that the lot has been "passed," "withdrawn," "returned to owner" or "bought-in."

AFTER THE AUCTION

Payment
Purchasers are expected to pay for your purchases the day after the sale and to remove the property you have bought by that date. Payment can be made by check, cash, money order or bank wire transfer. To avoid any delivery delays, prospective buyers are encouraged to supply bank or other suitable references before the auction.

Extended Payment Terms
With the consent of the consignor, Christie's may offer extended credit terms to prospective buyers whose creditworthiness has been verified. These terms will generally provide for the payment of the final bid price in three equal monthly installments. For further information, please contact the specialist department or Christie's Credit Department at (212) 546 1040 prior to the date of the auction.

Shipping
After payment has been made in full, Christie's may, as a service to buyers, arrange to have property packed, insured and shipped at your request and expense. For your convenience, a shipping form is enclosed with your invoice and is also available through our Art Transport Department at (212) 546 1113. In circumstances in which Christie's arranges and bills for such services via invoice or credit card, we will also include an administration charge.

We recommend that you request an estimate for any large items or property of high value requiring specialized professional packers.

Collection
Due to space constraints, Christie's will move sold property out of the saleroom five days after the sale.

After 5 business days from the sale, uncollected purchases will incur administration, handling and insurance charges for each day until the lots are picked up. These charges are explained in detail under Christie's Charges and Sales Tax at the back of this catalogue. A lot will not be released until all charges for the lot are settled.

Sale Results
Price lists are sent automatically to catalogue subscribers and absentee bidders shortly after each sale and are available to others on request. The price list will not include lots that were withdrawn or failed to sell. The price paid for any bought-in lot sold within 24 hours of the auction may be included on the list of prices realized but will be marked to indicate that such price was not realized at the auction. In addition, interested clients can obtain spoken sale results for specific lots as well as faxed price lists for entire sales both in the United States and internationally by calling (212) 452 4100, Christie's Sales Results line.

CONDITIONS OF SALE

These Conditions of Sale and Limited Warranty, together with any Glossary which may appear on the following pages, are Christie's and the Consignor's entire agreement with the buyer with respect to the property listed in this catalogue. The Conditions of Sale and Limited Warranty and all other contents of this catalogue may be amended by posted notices or oral announcements made during the sale. The property will be offered by us as agent for the Consignor, unless the catalogue indicates otherwise. By bidding at auction, you agree to be bound by these terms and conditions.

1. The authenticity of the authorship of property listed in the catalogue is guaranteed only as stated in the Limited Warranty and otherwise all property is sold "AS IS" without any representations or warranties by us or the Consignor as to merchantability, fitness for a particular purpose, description, size, quality, rarity, importance, medium, provenance, exhibition history, literature or historical relevance of any property. No statement set forth in this catalogue or made at the auction or in the bill of sale or otherwise, whether oral or written, shall be deemed such a warranty, representation or assumption of liability. We and the Consignor make no representations and warranties, express or implied, as to whether the purchaser acquires any copyrights for any reproduction rights in any property. Neither we nor the Consignor are responsible for errors and omissions in the catalogue, glossary or any supplemental material.
2. The purchase price payable by a buyer will be the sum of the final bid price plus the buyer's premium, together with any applicable sales or compensating use tax. The buyer's premium is 15% of the final bid price up to and including $50,000 plus 10% of any amount in excess of $50,000.
3. We reserve the right to withdraw any property before or at the sale and shall have no liability whatsoever for such withdrawal.
4. We reserve the right to reject any bid.

The highest bidder acknowledged by the auctioneer will be the buyer. In the event of any dispute between bidders, or any other issue with respect to the bidder, the auctioneer will have absolute discretion to determine the successful bidder, to continue the bidding, to cancel the sale or to reoffer and resell the article in dispute. If any dispute arises after the sale, our sale record is conclusive.

5. Although in our discretion we will execute absentee bids (written bids left with us prior to sale) or accept telephone bids as a convenience to clients who are not present at auction, we are not responsible for failing to execute such bids or for any errors or omissions in connection therewith.
6. Each lot marked with •
next to the lot number is offered subject to a reserve, which is the confidential minimum price below which the lot will not be sold. Christie's shall act to protect the reserve by bidding through the auctioneer. The auctioneer may open bidding on any lot below the reserve by placing a bid on behalf of the Consignor. The auctioneer may continue to bid on behalf of the Consignor up to the amount of the reserve, either by placing consecutive bids or by placing bids in response to other bidders.
7. Title to the offered lot passes to the buyer upon the fall of the auctioneer's hammer and the announcement by the auctioneer that the lot has been sold, subject to compliance by the buyer with all other Conditions of Sale. The buyer assumes full risk and responsibility for the lot and shall immediately pay the full purchase price or such part as we, in our sole discretion, require. In addition, the buyer may be required to sign a confirmation of purchase. We reserve the right to impose a late charge of 16% per annum of the total purchase price if payment is not made in accordance with this paragraph.
8. No lot may be removed from our premises until the buyer has paid the purchase price in full or has satisfied such terms as we, in our sole discretion, shall require. Subject to the fore-

going, all lots are to be paid for no later than 5:00 p.m. on the day following the sale. We may move the property to an off-site warehouse at the risk of the buyer. If a lot has not been collected by 5:00 p.m. five days following the sale, the buyer will be liable for administration fee of $30 and handling and insurance charges of at least $3 per day for each lot so remaining. These charges will continue until the lot is collected, and must be settled in full before the lot will be released.

9. We are not responsible for our acts or omissions in the handling, packing or shipping of purchased lots or those of other handlers, packers or carriers of purchased lots. Packing and handling of purchased lots are at the entire risk of the buyer. If Christie's arranges and bills for such services via invoice or credit card, Christie's will include an administration charge. If we obtain on behalf of the purchaser an export license for an item containing an endangered species, there will be a charge of $150 for each license obtained.
10. If the buyer fails to comply with any of these Conditions of Sale, we may, in addition to asserting all remedies available by law, including the right to hold such defaulting buyer liable for the purchase price, (i) cancel the sale, retaining as liquidated damages any payment made by the buyer, (ii) resell the property without reserve at public auction or privately on seven days' notice to the buyer, (iii) pay the Consignor an amount equal to the net proceeds payable in respect of the amount bid by the defaulting buyer and then resell the property to a third party without reserve at public auction or privately on seven days' notice to such buyer or (iv) take such other action as we deem necessary or appropriate. If we resell the property pursuant to clause (ii) or (iii) above, the defaulting buyer shall be liable for the payment of any deficiency between the purchase price and the price obtained upon resale pursuant to clause (ii) or (iii) above and all costs and expenses, including administration, handling, insurance, warehous-

ing, the expenses of both sales, reasonable attorneys' fees, commissions, incidental damages and all other charges due hereunder. In the event that such buyer pays a portion of the purchase price for any or all lots purchased, we shall apply the payment received to such lot or lots that we, in our sole discretion, deem appropriate. Any buyer who fails to comply with these Conditions of Sale will be deemed to have granted us a security interest in, and we may retain as collateral security for such buyer's obligation to us, any property in our possession owned by such buyer. We shall have the benefit of all rights of a secured party under the Uniform Commercial Code adopted in the state where the auction is held.

11. The respective rights and obligations of the parties with respect to the Conditions of Sale and the conduct of the auction shall be governed and interpreted by the laws of the state in which the auction is held. By bidding at an auction, whether present in person or by agent, by absentee bid, telephone or other means, the buyer shall be deemed to have consented to the exclusive jurisdiction of the courts of such state and the Federal courts sitting in such state. The buyer expressly agrees that (i) neither we nor the Consignor shall be liable, in whole or in part, for any special, indirect or consequential damages, including, without limitation, loss of profits and (ii) the buyer's damages are limited exclusively to the original purchase price paid for the lot.

LIMITED WARRANTY

Christie's warrants the authenticity of authorship on the terms and conditions and to the extent set forth herein. Subject to the provisions of the last paragraph hereof, Christie's warrants for a period of five years from the date of sale that any property described in headings printed in UPPER CASE TYPE in this catalogue (as such description may be amended by any saleroom notice or announcement) which is unqualifiedly stated to be the work of a named author or authorship, is authentic and not counterfeit. The term "author" or "authorship" refers to the creator of the property or to the period, culture, source or origin, as the case may be, with which the creation of such property is identified in the description of the property in this catalogue. Only UPPER CASE TYPE headings of lots in this catalogue (i.e., headings having capital-letter type) indicate the degree of authenticity of authorship warranted by Christie's. If this catalogue has a glossary, the terms used in such headings are further explained therein. Any heading which is stated in the Glossary to represent a qualified opinion is not subject to the warranty contained herein. Christie's warranty does not apply to supplemental material which appears below the UPPER CASE TYPE heading of each lot in this catalogue and Christie's is not responsible for any errors or omissions in such supplemental material.

The benefits of this warranty are not assignable and shall be applicable only to the original buyer of the lot and not subsequent assigns, purchasers, heirs, owners or others who have or may acquire an interest therein. This warranty is conditioned upon the buyer returning the lot to Christie's, 502 Park Avenue, New York, N.Y. 10022, in the same condition as at the time of sale.

The buyer's sole and exclusive remedy against Christie's and the seller under this warranty shall be the rescission of the sale and the refund of the original purchase price paid for the lot. This remedy shall be in lieu of any other remedy which might otherwise be available as a matter of law, and neither Christie's nor the seller shall be liable, in whole or in part, for any special, incidental or consequential damages, including, without limitation, loss of profits.

Except as otherwise specifically provided herein, all property is sold "as is" and neither Christie's nor the seller makes any express or implied warranty or representation of any kind or nature with respect to the property. In no event shall Christie's or the seller be responsible for the correctness of, or be deemed to have made, any representation or warranty of merchantability, fitness for purpose, description, size, medium, genuineness, attribution, provenance or condition concerning the property, and no statement set forth in this catalogue or made at the sale or in the bill of sale or invoice or elsewhere, whether oral or written, shall be deemed such a warranty or representation or an assumption of liability. Christie's and the seller make no warranty or representation, express or implied, that the buyer of any work of art or other property will acquire any copyright or reproduction rights thereto.

Christie's limited warranty does not apply to the (i) attribution of authorship of paintings, drawings, graphic art or sculpture created before 1870, unless such works are determined to be counterfeit, as such attribution is based on current scholarly opinion, which may change, (ii) attribution of authorship of paintings, drawings, graphic art or sculpture created after 1870 if such attribution at the date of the auction was in accordance with then generally accepted scholarly opinion or fairly indicated there to be a conflict of such opinion or (iii) identification of the period or dates of the execution of any property which may be proven inaccurate by means of a scientific process which was not generally accepted for use until after the date of the auction, unreasonably expensive or impractical to use or likely to have caused damage to the property.

CHRISTIE'S CHARGES AND SALES TAX FOR THIS SALE

CHRISTIE'S CHARGES

Buyers

Christie's charges a premium to the buyer on the final bid price of each lot sold at the following rates: 15% of the final bid price up to and including $50,000 and 10% of the final bid price above $50,000.

Administration, Handling and Insurance Charges

For 5 calendar days after the auction, uncollected purchases are held at our gallery or warehouse premises free of charge. Thereafter, uncollected purchases will incur handling, administration and insurance charges, which will be managed by Cadogan Tate on behalf of Christie's, at the rates specified below.

Unsold lots which are not collected within 5 days after the auction will also incur handling, administration and insurance charges at the following rates:

Dresses:
Administration: $30.00
Handling per day: $3.00

All lots:
Insurance: Lower of 0.5% of insured value/total of above charges.

New York State Sales Tax: 8.25% of above charges.

Note to all buyers:
Buyers are reminded of their responsibility for purchased lots as outlined in paragraphs 7 and 8 of our Conditions of Sale, printed in this catalogue. At the fall of the auctioneer's hammer, the buyer assumes full responsibility for the lot.

Beginning on the 6th day after the auction, all lots are insured at the purchase price, including the buyer's premium. In the event of any damage, Christie's will be liable at our sole option only for the cost of repairing or restoring the property.

Lots may only be collected with the approval of the Purchase Payments office at Christie's, which will be given only when all amounts due Christie's and Cadogan Tate, as agent of Christie's, have been paid in full. Charges may be paid in advance or at the time of collection by cash, cheque, wire transfer, credit card, bank draft, or traveller's cheque. Please call 888-278-7887 to ascertain the amount due.

SALES TAX

Buyers

Christie's is offering all lots in this catalogue as agent for an organization holding a State of New York Exempt Organization Certificate. Accordingly, no sales tax is due on the purchase price of the lots if the property is picked up or delivered in the State of New York. However, a sales or use tax is due from the buyer if any such lot is shipped to New Jersey or Connecticut or any of the following states where Christie's maintains offices: Alabama, California, Florida, Illinois, Massachusetts, Pennsylvania, Rhode Island, Texas and Washington D.C.

Charitable Status

Although a portion of sale proceeds of any lot and profits from the catalogue will benefit an American charity, any purchaser who is a U.S. taxpayer may not deduct any portion of the purchase price of any lot or the cost of the catalogue as a charitable donation within the meaning of Section 170 of the Internal Revenue Code.

Consignors

As agent for the consignor, Christie's is responsible for the collection and remittance of sales or use tax from the buyer.

ABSENTEE BID FORM

Client # _____

CHRISTIE'S

502 Park Avenue, New York, New York 10022

billing name (please print)
_____

address
_____

city _____ state _____ zip code _____

daytime telephone
_____

evening telephone _____ fax # _____

signature
_____

AMFAR-9074   **18 MARCH 1999**

sale title and code   sale date

SALE TITLE   Unforgettable:
               Fashion of the Oscars®

DATE   **Thursday 18 March 1998
            at 6.00 p.m. (By ticket only)**

CODE NAME   **AMFAR**

SALE NO.   **9074**

[Dealers: Billing name and address should agree with your state or local sales tax exemption certificate. Invoices cannot be changed after they have been printed.]

I request that Christie's enter bids on the following lots up to the maximum price I have indicated for each lot.

I understand that if my bid is successful, the purchase price will be the sum of my final bid plus a premium of 15% of the final bid price up to and including $50,000 and 10% of the amount above $50,000 ("buyer's premium") and any applicable state or local sales or use tax.

I understand that Christie's executes absentee bids as a convenience for clients and is not responsible for inadver-

tently failing to execute bids or for errors relating to execution of bids. On my behalf, Christie's will try to purchase these lots for the lowest possible price, taking into account the reserve and other bids.

If identical absentee bids are left, Christie's will give precedence to the first one received. All successful bids are subject to the terms of the Limited Warranty. Absence of Other Warranties and Conditions of Sale printed in the front of each Christie's catalogue.

A MINIMUM BID OF US$2,000 IS RECOMMENDED

Lot Number (in numerical order)	Bid $ (excluding buyer's premium)	Lot Number (in numerical order)	Bid $ (excluding buyer's premium)	Lot Number (in numerical order)	Bid $ (excluding buyer's premium)

To be sure that bids will be accepted and delivery of lots not delayed, bidders not yet known to Christie's should supply a bank reference.

name of bank(s)
_____

address of bank(s)
_____

accounts number(s)
_____

name of account officer(s)
_____

bank telephone number
_____

To allow time for processing, **absentee bids should be received at least 24 hours before the sale begins**. Christie's will confirm all bids received by fax by return fax. If you have not received our confirmation within one business day, please resubmit your bid(s) or contact the Bid Department at telephone (212) 546 1129 or fax (212) 832 2216.

CHRISTIE'S DEPARTMENTS

SPECIALIST DEPARTMENTS

Director of Specialist Departments
Christopher Hartop (212) 546 1019

American Furniture & Decorative Arts
Tel: (212) 546 1181
Fax: (212) 223 3985
John Hays
Martha Willoughby
Jennifer Olshin
Susan D. Kleckner, *American Folk Art*
▲ Dean F. Failey, *Senior Director*
(212) 702 5489

American Indian Art and Western Memorabilia
Tel: (212) 606 0536
Fax: (212) 517 8411
Elyse Luray Marx
Hadley Colburn Freeman
Stacy Marcus Chidekel, *Consultant*
Allen Wardwell, *Consultant*

American Paintings
Tel: (212) 546 1179
Fax: (212) 319 0858
Paul R. Provost
Eric Widing
Mia A. Schläppi
▲ Andrew Schoelkopf, *Senior Director*

Los Angeles
Tel: (310) 385 2655
Fax: (310) 385 0246
Catherine Leonhard

Antiquities
Tel: (212) 546 1075
Fax: (212) 446 9569
G. Max Bernheimer
Molly Morse

Art Nouveau, Art Deco, Arts & Crafts
Tel: (212) 546 1084
Fax: (212) 980 2043
Lars Rachen
Peggy Gilges
▲ Nancy A. McClelland, *Senior Director*

Books & Manuscripts
Tel: (212) 546 1195
Fax: (212) 980 2043
Francis Wahlgren
Chris Coover, *Manuscripts*
Anne Tozzi
Nina Musinsky, *Consultant*
Bart Auerbach, *Consultant*
Hope Mayo, *Consultant*
Stephen C. Massey, *Senior International Consultant*
▲ Felix de Marez Oyens, *Director, International Department*
(212) 546 1197

Chinese Ceramics & Works of Art
Tel: (212) 546 1160
Fax: (212) 888 7025
Athena Zonars
Sarah Wong
Patricia Curtin, *Consultant*
s Theow-Huang Tow, International Director

Los Angeles
Tel: (310) 385 0613
Fax: (310) 385 0246
Michael Hughes
(212) 546 1038

Chinese Paintings
Tel: (212) 546 1157
Fax: (212) 888 7025
Cheng-Ming Ma
Laura Whitman

Coins & Bank Notes (at Spink America)
Tel: (212) 546 1056
Fax: (212) 750 5874
Antony Wilson
Daniel Trout
Thomas Tesoriero

Contemporary Art
Tel: (212) 546 1168
Fax: (212) 319 0858
Andrew Massad
Philippe Ségalot
▲ Martha Baer, *Senior Director*
(212) 546 1144
▲ Laura Paulson, *Senior Specialist*

Los Angeles
Tel: (310) 385 2660
Fax: (310) 385 0246
Deborah McLeod
Robert Looker

European Ceramics & Glass
Tel: (212) 546 5821
Fax: (212) 223 3985
Jody Wilkie
Becky MacGuire, *Chinese Export*
Ellen Jenkins, *Consultant*
Lynne Stair, *Consultant*

European Furniture
Tel: (212) 546 1151
Fax: (212) 223 3985
Alistair Clarke
Melissa Gagen, *English Furniture*
Orlando Rock
Will Strafford, *French Furniture*
Natasha Schlesinger
Jessica Segal
Angus Wilkie, *Consultant*
John Hardy, *International Consultant*

Los Angeles
Tel: (310) 385 2678
Fax: (310) 385 9295
Andrea Fiuczynski

European Works of Art & Tapestries
Tel: (212) 546 1148
Fax: (212) 223 3985
Frances McCord Krongard
▲ Andrew Butterfield

Impressionist and Nineteenth Century Art
Tel: (212) 546 1173
Fax: (212) 888 6485
Franck Giraud
Nicholas Maclean
Cyanne Chutkow
John Steinert, *Drawings & Watercolors*
Pamela Bingham
Andrew Butterfield
Constantine Frangos
Christine Grounds
Meredith Harper-Wiley, *Drawings & Watercolors*
Andrew Rose, *Sporting Paintings*
▲ Michael Findlay, *International Director*
▲ Polly Sartori, *Senior Director*

Indian and Southeast Asian Art
Tel: (212) 702 2666
Fax: (212) 750 1522
Hugo Weihe

Japanese Art
Tel: (212) 546 1156
Fax: (212) 888 7025
Yoshinori Munemura
Susan Lewis
Julia Meech, *Consultant*
Jane Oliver, *Consultant*

Jewelry
Tel: (212) 546 1133
Fax: (212) 832 3560
Simon Teakle
Susan Abeles
Daphne Lingon
Riya Takaya

Boston
Tel: (617) 536 6000
Fax: (617) 536 0002
Susan Florence
Chicago
Tel: (312) 787 2765
Fax: (312) 951 7449
Susan Florence
Florida
Tel: (561) 833 6952
Fax: (561) 833 0007
Susan Florence
Los Angeles
Tel: (310) 385 2666
Fax: (310) 385 9295
Glenn Spiro
Brett O'Connor

Korean Art
Tel: (212) 546 1156
Fax: (212) 888 0927
Yoshinori Munemura
Heakyum Kim

Latin American Paintings
Tel: (212) 546 1099
Fax: (212) 888 0927
Juan Varez

Motor Cars
Tel: (310) 385 2699
Fax: (310) 385 0246
David Gooding
Miles Morris

Musical Instruments
Tel: (212) 702 2683
Fax: (212) 980 2043
Jonathan Stone

Nineteenth Century Furniture
Tel: (212) 606 0529
Fax: (212) 717 4725
Antonia M. Phillips

Old Master Paintings & Drawings
Tel: (212) 546 1178
Fax: (212) 319 0858
Anthony Crichton-Stuart
Sarah Lidsey
James Bruce-Gardyne
Alan Wintermute
Ilaria Quadrani, *Old Master Drawings*

Photographs
Tel: (212) 546 1063
Fax: (212) 980 2043
Rick Wester
Ellen de Boer
Leila Buckjune

Popular Arts
Tel: (212) 606 0543
Fax: (212) 517 8411
Simeon Lipman

Prints
Tel: (212) 546 1022
Fax: (212) 980 2043
Jonathan Rendell
Anne Spink
Christopher Gaillard
Kelly Troester
Susannah Eykyn

Rugs & Carpets
Tel: (212) 546 1187
Fax: (212) 223 3985
Elisabeth Poole

Russian Works of Art
Tel: (212) 702 2683
Fax: (212) 980 2043
Alexis de Tiesenhausen
Genevieve Wheeler

Silver and Objects of Vertu
Tel: (212) 546 1153
Fax: (212) 223 3985
Jeanne Sloane
Anna Eschapasse
Laura Verlaque
▲ Christopher Hartop

Stamps (at Spink America)
Tel: (212) 546 1087
Fax: (212) 750 5874
Brian Bleckwenn

Twentieth Century Art
Tel: (212) 546 1170
Fax: (212) 371 7261
Franck Giraud
Christopher Eykyn
Alison Buscher
John Steinert, *Drawings & Watercolors*
Richard Francis
Andrew Butterfield
Meredith Harper-Wiley, *Drawings & Watercolors*
Mary Peck
Guy Bennett
▲ Michael Findlay, *International Director*
▲ Martha Baer, *Senior Director*
▲ Laura Paulson, *Senior Specialist*

Los Angeles
Tel: (310) 385 2660
Fax: (310) 385 0246
Deborah McLeod
Robert Looker

Watches
Tel: (212) 546 1012
Fax: (212) 832 3560
Doug Escribano
Ruth Zandberg

Wine
Tel: (212) 546 5830
Fax: (212) 317 2470
Christopher Burr
Brian Robinson
Frederic C. Hatton, *Consultant*

Los Angeles
Tel: (310) 385 2600
Fax: (310) 385 9292
Cameron Hobel

CLIENT ADVISORY SERVICES

Tel: (212) 546 1036
Fax: (212) 750 1537
Kate Gubelmann
Kathy Kermian
Heidi Kucker
Kim Solow
Jennifer Kaplan
Sharon Kim
Gabriela Lobo
Elizabeth Sarnoff
Maria Los
Mirja Spooner
▲ Mary Libby
▲ Bonnie Stern
▲ Angus Wilkie

Estates & Appraisals
Tel: (212) 546 1060
Fax: (212) 750 6498
Marc B. Porter
Amy Corcoran, Attorney/Banker Services
Linda Izzo, Appraisals
Deborah Ahearn, Fine Arts Appraisals
Thomas Root, Decorative Arts Appraisals
▲ Stephen S. Lash

Los Angeles
Tel: (310) 385 2611
Fax: (310) 385 9292
Brooke Glassman Kanter

Financial Services
Tel: (212) 702 1392
Fax: (212) 754 2390
Ray Horne
Patricia G. Hambrecht

Internet Access
http://www.christies.com

Museum & Corporate Services
Tel: (212) 546 1190
Fax: (212) 446 9569
Allison Whiting

ADMINISTRATIVE DEPARTMENTS

General Counsel
Tel: (212) 546 1193
Fax: (212) 223 7289
Jo Backer Laird

Human Resources
Tel: (212) 546 1106
Fax: (212) 421 8722
Cindy Weiss Drankoski

Marketing & Public Relations
Tel: (212) 702 1385
Fax: (212) 421 8722
Susan Korb
Taggarty Patrick

Special Events
Tel: (212) 546 1007
Fax: (212) 446 9566

AUCTIONEERS

Susan Abeles (#924040)
Noël Annesley (#0950782)
James Bruce-Gardyne (#0940126)
Christopher Burge (#761543)
François Curiel (#761369)
Catherine D. Elkies (#866011)
Dean Failey (#799256)
Andrea Fiuczynski (#849132)
Christopher Hartop (#779124)
John Hays (#822982)
Ursula Hermacinski (#917819)
Sarah Lidsey (#0953093)
Elyse Lauray-Marx (#0995713)
Nicholas Maclean (#925516)
Stephen C. Massey (#768546)
Patrick S. Meade (#866012)
Barbara Strongin (#849133)
Simon Teakle (#867918)
Francis Wahlgren (#868229)

SALEROOMS AND REPRESENTATIVES

NORTH AMERICA AND SOUTH AMERICA
Salerooms

Christie's Inc.
502 Park Avenue
New York, New York 10022
Tel: (212) 546 1000
Fax: (212) 980 8163
Christopher Burge, *Chairman*
Stephen S. Lash, Vice *Chairman*
Patricia G. Hambrecht, *President*
Geoffrey Iddison,
Chief Operating Officer
Christopher Hartop,
Executive Vice President

Christie's East
219 East 67th Street
New York, New York 10021
Tel: (212) 606 0400
Fax: (212) 737 6076
Catherine D. Elkies, *President*

Christie's Los Angeles
Marcia Wilson Hobbs, *Chairman*
Dermot Chichester, *Managing Director*
Andrea Fiuczynski, *Director of Business Development*
360 North Camden Drive
Beverly Hills, California 90210
Tel: (310) 385 2600
Fax: (310) 385 9292

Christie's Education
Tel: (310) 385 2697
Fax: (310) 385 9327

Other Services
Christie's Education
502 Park Avenue
New York, New York 10022
Tel: (212) 546 1092
Fax: (212) 980 7845
Sandra Joys, *Director*

Christie's Great Estates
1850 Old Pecos Trail, Suite D
Santa Fe, NM 87505
Tel: (505) 983 8733
Fax: (505) 982 0348
Kay Coughlin, *President*

Christie's Images
13-06 43rd Avenue
Long Island City, New York 11101
Tel: (718) 472 5030
Fax: (718) 472 9005
E-mail: chrisimage@earthlink.net
Website: www.christies.com/christiesimages/
Peter Rohowsky, *Managing Director*

Representatives
Atlanta
Alison M. Thompson
P.O. Box 550652
Atlanta, Georgia 30355
Tel: (404) 846 0780
Fax: (404) 846 0790

Baltimore/Washington, D.C.
Tel: (202) 333 7459
Fax: (202) 342 0537

Boston/New England
Elizabeth M. Chapin
Susan Florence, *Jewelry*
Brigitte Bradford, International Rep.
216 Newbury Street
Boston, Massachusetts 02116-2543
Tel: (617) 536 6000
Fax: (617) 536 0002

Chicago/Midwest
Gary Piattoni
Mary Ahern, *Estates and Appraisals*
Laura de Frise
Frances Blair
Susan Florence, *Jewelry*
875 N. Michigan Ave., Suite 3810
Chicago, Illinois 60611-1803
Tel: (312) 787 2765
Fax: (312) 951 7449
Toll Free (877) 787 0001
(outside Illinois)

Dallas
Carolyn Foxworth
5500 Preston Road, Suite 210
Dallas, Texas 75205
Tel: (214) 521 1843
Fax: (214) 521 8265

Delaware
Andrew C. Rose
P.O. Box 4357
Greenville, Delaware 19807
Tel: (302) 421 5719
Fax: (302) 421 5719

Houston
Lisa Cavanaugh
5900 Memorial Drive Suite 203
Houston, Texas 77007
Tel: (713) 802 0191
Fax: (713) 802 0193

Miami
Vivian Pfeiffer
Susan Florence, *Jewelry*
Jean Kislak, *International Rep.*
Alina Pedroso Arellano,
International Rep.
110 Merrick Way, Suite 2A
Coral Gables, Florida 33134
Tel: (305) 445 1487
Fax: (305) 441 6561

Minneapolis
Kelly Perry
Carol Bemis, *Consultant*
706 Second Avenue South
Suite 710
Minneapolis, Minnesota 55402
Tel: (612) 664 0478
Fax: (612) 664 0479

Montgomery
Carol W. Ballard
P.O. Box 231207
Montgomery, Alabama 36123
Tel: (334) 244 9688
Fax: (334) 244 9588

New Orleans
Susan Gore Brennan
240A Chartres Street
New Orleans, Louisiana 70130
Tel: (504) 522 0008
Fax: (504) 522 8005

Newport
Betsy D. Ray
Ralph Carpenter, Consultant
228 Spring Street
Newport, Rhode Island 02840
Tel: (401) 849 9222
Fax: (401) 849 6322

Oklahoma City
Konrad Keesee, *International Rep.*
6421 Avondale Drive
Oklahoma City, Oklahoma 73116
Tel: (405) 843 1574
Fax: (405) 842 1775

Palm Beach
Meg Bowen
Susan Florence, *Jewelry*
Helen Cluett, *International Rep.*
440 Royal Palm Way, Suite 103
Palm Beach, Florida 33480
Tel: (561) 833 6952
Fax: (561) 833 0007

Philadelphia
Susan Ravenscroft
Alison L. Manaker, *Estates and Appraisals*
Paul Ingersoll, *Consultant*
P.O. Box 1112
Bryn Mawr, Pennsylvania 19010
Tel: (610) 525 5493
Fax: (610) 525 0967

San Francisco/Pacific Northwest
Laura Knoop King
400 Montgomery Street, Suite 920
San Francisco, California 94104
Tel: (415) 982 0982
Fax: (415) 982 8982

Santa Barbara
Carlyle C. Eubank
P.O. Box 1598
Santa Ynez, California 93460
Tel: 805 688 2728
Fax: 805 686 4548

Seattle
Catherine Vare
2802 East Madison Street Suite 107
Seattle, WA 98112
Tel: (206) 323 2264
Fax: (206) 320 0725

St. Louis
Tel: (312) 787 2765
Fax: (312) 951 7449
Toll Free (877) 787 0001
(outside Illinois)

Washington, D.C./Baltimore
Cathy Sledz
Brittain Cudlip, *International Rep.*
Nuala Pell, *International Rep.*
Joan Gardner, *International Rep.*
Hamilton Court
1228 31st Street N.W.
Washington, D.C. 20007
Tel: (202) 333 7459
Fax: (202) 342 0537

Argentina
Arroyo 850
1007 Capital
Buenos Aires, Argentina
Tel: (541) 393 4222
Fax: (541) 394 9578

Bermuda
Betsy Ray
Tel: (401) 849 9222
Fax: (401) 849 6322

Brazil
Rio de Janeiro
Candida Sodré
Maria Teresa Sodré
Rue Icatu 39, APT. 203
Rio de Janeiro 22260-190
Tel: (5521) 539 9583
Fax: (5521) 286 8237

São Paulo
Paulo Figueiredo
Maria Teresa Sozio
Alameda Casa Branca 851 cj. 24/25
01408-001 São Paulo, Brazil
Tel: (5511) 881 0435
Fax: (5511) 852 7244

Canada
Montreal
Leah Carey
Brenda Norris, International Rep.
Tel: (800) 960 2063

Toronto
Suzanne E. Davis
170 Bloor Street West, Suite 210
Toronto, Ontario M5S IT9
Tel: (416) 960 2063
Fax: (416) 960 8815
Tel: (800) 960 2063 (Canada)

Vancouver
Jodi M. Norrison
555 West Hastings Street, Suite 700
Vancouver, British Columbia V6B 4N5
Tel: (604) 605 3330
Fax: (604) 605 3331
Tel: (888) 382 9222 (Canada)

Chile
Denise Ratinoff de Lira
Martin de Zamora
3611 Los Condes
Santiago de Chile
Tel: (562) 231 7349
Fax: (562) 232 2671

Mexico
Mexico City
Patricia Hernández
Miguel Cervantes, Consultant
Christie's Mexico
Galileo 54, piso 2
Col. Polanco, 11560 México, D.F.
Tel: (525) 281 5503, 281 5463
Fax: (525) 281 5454

Monterrey
Alejandra Sanchez Morales
Privada de Capellania #401
Col. Santa Barbara
Garza Garcia, N.L. C.P. 66220
Tel: (525) 8338 5357/8338 5229
Fax: (525) 8338 7732

Uruguay
Cristina G. de Berenbau
Gral. French 1767
Montevideo 11500
Tel: (598) 2600 7723
Fax: (598) 2600 7723

Venezuela
Alain Jathière, International Rep.
Quinta las Magnolias
Calle Los Olivos
Los Chorros, Caracas
Tel: (582) 238 03 55
Fax: (582) 235 76 13

Regional Offices
Mary Hoeveler, *Director*
Monique Foster, *Regional Coordinator*
Tel: (212) 702 5496
Fax: (212) 750 6498

International Representatives
Nan Kempner, *New York*
Mary Libby, *New York*
Bonnie Stern, *New York*
Angus Wilkie, *New York*
Brigitte Bradford, *Boston*
Alina Pedroso Arellano, *Miami*
Jean Kislak, *Miami*
Helen Cluett, *Palm Beach*
Brittain Cudlip, *Washington, D.C.*
Joan Gardner, *Washington, D.C.*
Nuala Pell, *Washington, D.C.*
Konrad Keesee, *Oklahoma City*
Brenda Norris, *Montreal*
Terry Stanfill, *Los Angeles*
Alain Jathière, *Caracas*

ASIA AND PACIFIC
Salerooms

Australia
Melbourne
The Lord Poltimore, *Chairman*
Roger McIlroy, *Managing Director*
Christie's Australia Pty. Ltd.
1 Darling Street
South Yarra, Victoria 3141
Tel: (613) 9820 4311
Fax: (613) 9820 4876

Sydney
180 Jersey Road
Woollahra, N.S.W. 2025
Tel: (612) 9326 1422
Fax: (612) 9327 8439

Hong Kong
Anthony Lin, *Managing Director*
Ben Kong, *Chinese Paintings*
Edmond Chin,
Western & Jadeite Jewelry
Christie's Hong Kong Ltd.
2203–5 Alexandra House
16–20 Chater Road, Central

Hong Kong
Tel: (852) 2521 5396
Fax: (852) 2845 2646

Singapore
Irene Lee, Managing Director
Cecilia Ong, Consultant
Christie's International
Singapore Pte Ltd.
Unit 3, Parklane,
Goodwood Park Hotel
22 Scotts Road, Singapore 228221
Tel: (65) 235 3828
Fax: (65) 235 8128

WORLDWIDE
Representatives

Asia Regional Office
Anthony Lin, Deputy Chairman
Philip Ng, Managing Director, Asia
501 Orchard Road
15-02 Wheelock Place
Singapore 238880
Tel: (65) 737 3884
Fax: (65) 733 7975

Australia
Adelaide
James and Ian Bruce
444-446 Pulteney Street
Adelaide S.A. 5000
Tel: (618) 8232 2860
Fax: (618) 8232 6506

Brisbane
Nicole Roberts
1st Floor
482 Brunswick Street
Fortitude Valley
Queensland 4006
Tel: (617) 3254 1499
Fax: (617) 3254 1566

Perth
Cherry Lewis
68 Mount Street
Perth WA 6000
Tel: (618) 9321 5764
Fax: (618) 9322 1387

People's Republic of China
Beijing
Lillian Chin
Christie, Manson & Woods Ltd.
16B CITIC Building
19 Jianguomenwai Dajie
Beijing 100004

China
Tel: (8610) 6500 6517
Fax: (8610) 6500 6034

Shanghai
Lillian Chin
Christie's Shanghai Limited
Suite 404
Shanghai Centre
1376 Nanjing Road West
Shanghai 200040
Tel: (8621) 6279 8773
Fax: (8621) 6279 8771

India
Amrita Jhaveri
Christie's Bombay
3 Shelleys Estate
30 P. J. Ramchandani Marg
Mumbai 400-039
Tel: (91 22) 285 5649
Fax: (91 22) 288 1387
Rohni Khosla (Consultant)
Tel: (91 11) 687 4316
Fax: (91 11) 687 4316

Indonesia
Jakarta
Mrs. Deborah Iskandar
Christie, Manson & Woods Ltd.
The Regent Jakarta
Jl Rasuna Said
Jakarta 12920
Indonesia
Tel: (6221) 527 2606
Fax: (6221) 527 2605

Japan
Sachiko Hibiya, *President*
Roddy Ropner, *Managing Director*
Christie's Japan Limited
Sankyo Ginza Bldg. 4F
6-5-13 Ginza,
Chuo-ku, Tokyo 104-0061
Tel: (813) 3571 0668
Fax: (813) 3571 5853

Lebanon
Beirut
P.O. Box 11-3252
Beirut
Tel: (96) 11 737 859
Fax: (96) 11 737 860

Malaysia
Lim Meng Hong
Tunku Zahiah Sulong, *Consultant*
Christie Manson & Woods Ltd
Lobby-Unit 2 Renaissance Hotel
Jalan Sultan Ismail
Kuala Lumpur 50450
Malaysia
Tel: (603) 266 6300
Fax: (603) 266 3630

South Africa
Cape Town
Juliet Lomberg
14 Hillwood Road
Claremont
Cape Town 7700
Tel: (2721) 761 2676
Fax: (2721) 762 7129

Durban
Gillian Scott-Berning
P.O. Box 50227
Musgrave Road
Durban 4062
Tel: (2731) 207 8427
Fax: (2731) 207 8427

Johannesburg
Harriet Hedley
P.O. Box 72126
Parkview
Johannesburg 2122
Tel: (2711) 486 0967
Fax: (2711) 646 0390

South Korea
Mrs. Shin Duk Young
Christie's Korea
Hotel Shilla, 5F
202, 2-Ga, Jangchung-Dong
Chung-ku
Seoul, 100-392 Korea
Tel: (82) 2 230 3139
Fax: (82) 2 230 3138

Taiwan
Anthony Lin, *Managing Director*
Nancy Chen, *General Manager*
Christie's Hong Kong Ltd.
Taiwan Branch
13/F. No. 207 Tun Hua South Road
sec. 2, Suite 1302
Taipei, Taiwan
Tel: (8862) 2736 3356
Fax: (8862) 2736 4856

UNITED KINGDOM
Salerooms

Head Office
King Street
Christie, Manson & Woods Ltd.
8 King Street, St. James's
London SW1Y 6QT
Tel: (0171) 839 9060
Fax: (0171) 839 1611
Christopher Balfour, *Chairman*
François Curiel, *Vice Chairman*
John Lumley, *Vice Chairman*
Maria Reinshagen, *Vice Chairman*
The Earl of Halifax, *Vice Chairman*
Charles Cator, *Deputy Chairman*
Anthony Streatfeild, *Deputy Chairman*
The Lord Poltimore,
Deputy Chairman
Edward Dolman, *Managing Director*

South Kensington
Christie's South Kensington Ltd.
85 Old Brompton Road
London SW7 3LD
Tel: (0171) 581 7611
Fax: (0171) 321 3321
W.A. Coleridge, F.R.I.C.S. *President*
D.M.C. Chichester, *Chairman*
P.A. Barthaud, *Managing Director*

Scotland
Glasgow
Christie's Scotland Ltd.
164-166 Bath Street, Glasgow G2 4TB
Tel: (0141) 332 8134
Fax: (0141) 332 5759
D.M.C. Chichester, Chairman
P. Arbuthnot, Managing Director

Other Services
Christie's Education
63 Old Brompton Road
London SW7 3JS
Tel: (0171) 581 3933
Fax: (0171) 589 0383
Irmgard Pickering, *Managing Director*

Christie's Fine Art
Security Services Limited
42 Ponton Road
Nine Elms
London SW8 5BA
Tel: (0171) 622 0609
Fax: (0171) 978 2073
Gordon Brennan-Jesson
Colin Reeve
Sydney Gill

Christie's Images
1 Langley Lane
London SW8 1TH
Tel: (0171) 582 1282
Fax: (0171) 582 5632
E-mail: cImage@Compuserve.com
Website:www.christies.com/
christiesimages/
Shaunagh Money-Coutts,
Managing Director
Camilla Young, *Manager*

ENGLAND & WALES
Representatives

South East
South East Area Office

Sussex & Surrey
•Mark Wrey
North Street
Petworth
West Sussex GU28 0DD
Tel: (01798) 344440
Fax: (01798) 344442

Channel Islands
Melissa Bonn
Richard de la Hey
58 David Place, St. Helier
Jersey
Tel: (01534) 877582
Fax: (01534) 877540

Hampshire & Berkshire
Richard Wills
Middleton Estate Office
Longparish, Andover
Hampshire SP11 6PL
Tel: (01264) 720211
Fax: (01264) 720271

Kent
‡Christopher Proudfoot
The Old Rectory
Fawkham, Longfield
Kent DA3 8LX
Tel: (01474) 702854
Fax: (01474) 702854

Mrs. Gail Jessel
Ladham House
Goudhurst
Kent TN17 1DB
Tel: (01580) 212 595
Fax: (01580) 212 596

South West
South West Area Office

West Country and Wiltshire
•Richard de Pelet
Huntsman's Lodge, Inwood
Templecombe, Somerset BA8 0PF
Tel: (01963) 370518
Fax: (01963) 370605

South Dorset & South Hampshire
Nigel Thimbleby
Wolfeton House, Nr. Dorchester
Dorset DT2 9QN
Tel: (01305) 268748
Fax: (01305) 265090

Devon & Cornwall
The Hon. George Lopes, A.R.I.C.S.
Gnaton Estate Office
Yealmpton, Plymouth
Devon PL8 2HU
Tel: (01752) 880636
Fax: (01752) 880968

Central & Eastern
Central & Eastern Area Office

South Midlands & South Wales
•The Earl Fortescue
Simon Reynolds
111 The Promenade
Cheltenham, Glos. GL50 1PS
Tel: (01242) 518999
Fax: (01242) 576240

East Midlands
Rupert Hanbury
The Old Dairy
Elton
Peterborough PE8 6SQ
Tel: (01832) 280 876
Fax: (01832) 280 877
*Mrs. William Proby

East Anglia
Charles Bingham-Newland
Sackville Place
44-48 Magdalen Street
Norwich NR3 1JU
Tel: (01603) 614546
Fax: (01603) 618176
*Thomas Fellowes

Essex & Hertfordshire
James Service
Hawkins Harvest
Great Bardfield
Essex CM7 4QW
Tel: (01371) 810189
Fax: (01371) 810028

North
North Area Office

North-West Midlands
& North Wales
•Richard Roundell, F.R.I.C.S.
Jane Blood
Dorfold Hall, Nantwich
Cheshire CW5 8LD
Tel: (01270) 627 024
Fax: (01270) 628 723

Isle of Man
The Marchioness Conyngham
Myrtle Hill, Andreas Road
Ramsey, Isle of Man IM8 3UA
Tel: (01624) 814502
Fax: (01624) 814502

Yorkshire
◇Thomas Scott, F.S.A. (Scot)
Stephanie Bilton
*Sir Nicholas Brooksbank, Bt.
Princes House
13 Princes Square, Harrogate,
North Yorkshire HG1 1LW
Tel: (01423) 509 699
Fax: (01423) 509 977
*Richard Compton
North West
Victor Gubbins, F.R.I.C.S.
Eden Lacy, Lazonby, Penrith
Cumbria CA10 1BZ
Tel: (01768) 898 800
Fax: (01768) 898 020

Northumbria
Aidan Cuthbert
Eastfield House, Main Street
Corbridge
Northumberland, NE45 5LA
Tel: (01434) 633181
Fax: (01434) 633891

Nottingham & Derbyshire
David Coke-Steel
Trusley Old Hall
Sutton-on-the-Hill
Ashbourne
Derbyshire DE6 5JG
Tel: (01283) 733783
Fax: (01283) 733076

SCOTLAND
Representatives

Edinburgh & the Borders
Bernard Williams
Robert Lagneau
5 Wemyss Place
Edinburgh EH3 6DH
Tel: (0131) 225 4756/7
Fax: (0131) 225 1723

North of Scotland
Lady Eliza Leslie Melville
Lochluichart Lodge
By Garve
Ross-shire IV23 2PZ
Tel: (01997) 414370
Fax: (01997) 414340

South West Scotland
Charlotte Dickie
Poundland, Moniaive
Dumfriesshire DG3 4EG
Tel: (01848) 200 730
Fax: (01848) 200 731

Tayside, Fife & Grampian
Bernard Williams
Robert Lagneau
3/5 Mill Street
Perth PH1 5JB
Tel: (01738) 643088
Fax: (01738) 635227

NORTHERN IRELAND

Belfast
◇Danny Kinahan
Templepatrick
Co. Antrim BT39 0AH
Tel: (01849) 433480
Fax: (01849) 433410

THE REPUBLIC OF IRELAND

Glin
Desmond Fitz-Gerald, Knight of Glin
Glin Castle
Glin, Co. Limerick
Fax: (00353) 683 4364
52 Waterloo Road
Dublin 4
(Private Residence)
Tel: (00353) 1 668 0585
Fax: (00353) 1 668 0271

EUROPE
Salerooms

Greece
Athens
Elisavet Logotheti-Lyra,
Managing Director
Christie's Hellas Ltd.
26 Philellinon Street
10558 Athens
Tel: (301) 324 6900
Fax: (301) 324 6925

Israel
Mary Gilben
Christie's (Israel) Limited
Asia House, 4 Weizmann Street
Tel Aviv 64239
Tel: (9723) 6950695
Fax: (9723) 6952751

Italy
Rome
Franz Ziegler, *Managing Director*
Francesco Alverà
Christie's (International) S.A.,
Palazzo Massimo Lancellotti
Piazza Navona 114, Rome 00186
Tel: (3906) 687 2787
Fax: (3906) 686 9902
    (3906) 689 3080

Monaco
Pascal Bégo
Christie's Monaco S.A.M.
Park Palace, 98000 Monte-Carlo
Tel: (377) 97 97 11 00
Fax: (377) 97 97 11 01

The Netherlands
Amsterdam
Bernard Steyaert, *Managing Director*
Christie's Amsterdam B.V.
Cornelis Schuytstraat 57,
1071 JG Amsterdam
Tel: (3120) 57 55 255
Fax: (3120) 66 40 899

Switzerland
Geneva
François Curiel, President
Elisabeth Storm Nagy, *Vice President*
Franz Ziegler, Managing Director
Christie's (International) S.A.,
8 Place de la Taconnerie
1204 Geneva
Tel: (41 22) 319 17 66
Fax: (41 22) 319 17 67

Zurich
Maria Reinshagen,
Vice Chairman Christie's Europe
Dr. Brigit Bernegger, *Vice President*
Claudia Steinfels, *General Manager*
Christie's (Int.) A.G.
Steinwiesplatz, 8032 Zürich
Tel: (411) 268 1010
Fax: (411) 268 1011

Other Services
Christie's Education
France
Hôtel Salomon de Rothschild
11 Rue Berryer, 75008 Paris
Tel: (331) 42 25 10 90
Fax: (331) 42 25 10 91

EUROPE
Representatives

Austria
Dr. Johanna Schönburg-Hartenstein
Cornelia Pallavicini, Managing Director
Christie's Kunstauktionen GmbH
Bankgasse 1/Herrengasse 17
1010 Vienna
Tel: (431) 533 88 12
Fax: (431) 533 71 66

Belgium
Bernard Steyaert, Chairman
Bernard de Launoit, *Managing Director*
Géraldine André, Contemporary Art
Roland de Lathuy, Old Master Pictures
Christie's Belgium S.A.
33 Boulevard de Waterloo
1000 Brussels
Tel: (322) 512 8830
Fax: (322) 513 3279

Czech Republic
HSH The Princess Elisabeth Lobkowicz
Snemovni Ulice 11
Mala Strana, 11800 Praha-1
Czech Republic
Tel: (42-02) 57 09 61 27
Fax: (42-02) 57 09 61 28

Denmark
Birgitta Hillingsø
Dronningens Tværgade 10
1302 Copenhagen K
Tel: (45) 33 32 70 75
Fax: (45) 33 13 00 75

Finland
Barbro Schauman
Christie's
Vuorimiehenkatu 5A, 00140 Helsinki
Tel: (3589) 60 82 12
Fax: (3589) 66 06 87

France
Aix-en-Provence
Fabienne Albertini
28 rue Lieutaud, 13100
Aix en Provence
Tel: (33) 4 92 72 43 31
Fax: (33) 4 92 72 53 65

Bordeaux
Marie-Cecile Moueix
49 Cours Xavier Arnozan
33000 Bordeaux
Tel: (33) 5 56 81 65 47
Fax: (33) 5 56 51 15 71

Centre et Val de Loire
Nicole de Yturbe
Château de Montgraham
28400 Souance au Perche
Tel: (33) 2 37 29 13 66

Lyon
Vicomte Thierry de Lachaise
36 Place Bellecour
69002 Lyon
Tel: (33) 4 78 42 83 82
Fax: (33) 4 78 42 83 84

Paris
Hubert de Givenchy, *President*
Hugues Joffre, *President du Directoire*
Bertrand du Vignaud
Franck Prazan
Christie's France S.A.
6 Rue Paul Baudry, 75008 Paris
Tel: (33) 1 40 76 85 85
Fax: (33) 1 42 56 26 01

Germany
Dr. Johann Georg Prinz
von Hohenzollern,
Non Executive Chairman
Jörg-Michael Bertz, *Deputy Chairman*
Stefan Prinz von Ratibor,
General Manager
Birgid Seynsche-Vautz,
Administrative Manager

Berlin
Stefan Prinz von Ratibor,
General Manager
Marianne Kewenig
Victoria von Specht
Frederik Schwarz, *Jewelery*
Fasanenstraße 72, 10719 Berlin
Tel: (4930) 885 695 0
Fax: (4930) 885 695 95

Düsseldorf
Jörg-Michael Bertz, *Senior Specialist*
(19th and 20th Century Pictures)
Brigid Seynsche-Vautz,
Administrative Manager
Maike Borgwardt, *Valuation Manager*
Christie's (Deutschland) GmbH
P.O. Box 101810, Inselstraße 15
40479 Düsseldorf
Tel: (49211) 491 5930
Fax: (49211) 492 0339

Frankfurt
Charlotte Prinzessin von Croy
Gerard Goodrow
Nina von Oudarza
Arndtstraße 18
60325 Frankfurt am Main
Tel: (4969) 74 50 21
Fax: (4969) 75 20 79

Hamburg
Christiane Gräfin zu Rantzau
Wentzelstraße 21, 22301 Hamburg
Tel: (4940) 279 4073
Fax: (4940) 270 4497

Munich
Marie Christine Gräfin Huyn
Residenzstraße 27, 80333 München
Tel: (4989) 22 95 39
Fax: (4989) 29 63 02

Stuttgart
Claudia Freiin von Saint-Andre
Relenbergstrasse 69, 70174 Stuttgart
Tel: (49711) 226 9699
Fax: (49711) 226 0607

Greece
Thessaloniki
Christie's Thessaloniki
Aristotelous 8, 546 23 Thessaloniki
Tel: (3031) 244607
Fax: (3031) 242931

Italy
Bologna
Benedetta Possati Vittori Venenti
Casella Postale 642
40100 Bologna
Tel: (39051) 265154
Fax: (39051) 265630

Florence
Alessandra Niccolini di Camugliano
Casella Postale 62
56038 Ponsacco (PI)
Tel: (39587) 735487
Fax: (39587) 735487

Genoa
Rachele Guicciardi
Via Belvedere Montaldo, 5
16124 Genoa
Tel: (3910) 247 1204
Fax: (3910) 246 5351

Milan
Clarice Pecori Giraldi
Director Business Development
Franz Ziegler
Domenico Filipponi, *General Manager*
Christie's (Int.) S.A.
Piazza Santa Maria delle Grazie 1
20123 Milano
Tel: (3902) 46 70 141
Fax: (3902) 46 70 1429

Lazio
Alessandra Allaria
Via Cassiodoro 14, 00193 Rome
Tel: (396) 687 4147
Fax: (396) 683 2442

Turin
Sandro Perrone di San Martino
Via Maria Vittoria 4, 10123 Turin
Tel: (3911) 561 9453
Fax: (3911) 542 710

Veneto
Bianca Arrivabene Valenti Gonzaga
Casella Postale 602
30100 Venezia Centrale
Tel: (3941) 277 0086
Fax: (3941) 277 0086

Luxembourg
Countess Marina von Kamarowsky
16 rue Wurth-Paquet
2737 Luxembourg
Tel: (352) 44 04 95
Fax: (352) 44 04 92

The Netherlands
Bloemendaal
PO Box 116
2060 AC Bloemendaal
Tel: (3123) 526 0658
Fax: (3123) 526 0658

Rotterdam
PO Box 4019, 3006 AA Rotterdam
Tel: (3110) 212 0553
Fax: (3110) 212 0553

Norway
Benedicte Løvenskiold Dyvik
Christie's
Colbjornsengst, 1, N-0256 Oslo 2
Tel: (4722) 44 12 42
Fax: (4722) 55 92 36

Portugal
Mafalda Pereira Coutinho
Rua da Lapa 67, 1200 Lisbon
Tel: (3511) 396 9750
Fax: (3511) 396 9732

Spain
Barcelona
Piru Cantarell de Andreu
Mallorca, 235, 08008 Barcelona
Tel: (34) 9 34 87 82 59
Fax: (34) 9 34 87 85 04

Madrid
Casilda Fz-Villaverde y Silva
Pablo Melendo
Christie's Iberica S.L.
Antonio Maura 10, 28014 Madrid
Tel: (34) 9 15 32 66 26/7
Fax: (34) 9 15 23 12 40

Sweden
Stockholm
Lillemor Malmström
Sturegatan 26, 11436 Stockholm
Tel: (468) 662 0131
Fax: (468) 660 0725

South of Sweden
Baroness Irma Silfverschiold
230 41 Klagerup
Tel: (4640) 44 03 60
Fax: (4640) 44 03 71

South West of Sweden
Susanne Wiklund,
Forsvarsgatan 12
426 76 Vastra Frolunda, Gothenburg
Tel: (4631) 69 40 68
Fax: (4631) 694530

Switzerland
Lugano
Manoli Traxler
Christie's (Int.) S.A.
via soave, 9, 6900 Lugano
Tel: (4191) 922 2031
Fax: (4191) 922 2032

Geneve —see Salerooms

Zurich —see Salerooms

CHRISTIE'S NORTH AND SOUTH AMERICA

Christopher Burge, *Chairman*, Stephen S. Lash, *Vice Chairman*, Patricia G. Hambrecht President,
Geoffrey Iddison, *Chief Operating Officer*
Christopher Hartop, *Executive Vice President*
Michael Findlay, Theow-Huang Tow, *International Directors, Senior Vice Presidents*

Senior Vice Presidents
Martha Baer, Alistair Clarke, Cindy Weiss Drankoski, Dean Failey, Elisabeth D. Garrett, Franck Giraud, David Gooding,
John Hays, Marcia Wilson Hobbs, Mary Hoeveler, Ray Horne, Paul Ingersoll, Linda Izzo, Susan Korb, Jo Backer Laird,
Cheng-Ming Ma, Nancy A. McClelland, Marc Porter, Jonathan Rendell, Steven Russell, Polly Sartori, Andrew Schoelkopf,
Philippe Ségalot, Jeanne Sloane, Barbara Strongin, Simon Teakle

Regional Senior Vice Presidents
Lisa Cavanaugh, Elizabeth M. Chapin, Suzanne E. Davis, Susan Florence, Carolyn Foxworth,
Laura Knoop King, Gary Piattoni

Vice Presidents
Susan Adams, Susan Abeles, Deborah Ahearn, Mary Ahern, G. Max Bernheimer, Pamela Bingham, Alison Buscher,
Cyanne Chutkow, Chris Coover, Amy Corcoran, Anthony Crichton-Stuart, Woody Dunstan, Christopher Eykyn,
Sheri Farber, Andrea Fiuczynski, Richard Francis, Laura de Frise, Melissa Gagen, Peggy Gilges, Brooke Glassman,
Kate Gubelmann, Fernando Gutierrez, Ursula Hermacinski, Michael Hughes, Paul Jenkins, Sandra Joys, Kathy Kermian,
Susan D. Kleckner, Heidi Kucker, Daphne Lingon, Maria Ludkin, Nicholas Maclean, George McNeely, Patrick S. Meade,
Yoshinori Munemura, Taggarty Patrick, Laura Paulson, Vivian Pfeiffer, Paul Provost, Lars Rachen, Betsy Ray,
Orlando Rock, Thomas Root, Jean-René Saillard, Cathy Sledz, Kim Solow, Anne Spink, Joseph Stasko, John Steinert,
Will Strafford, Nancy Valentino, Catherine Vare, Francis Wahlgren, Hugo Weihe, Rick Wester, Marissa Wilcox,
Jody Wilkie, Ken Yeh, Athena Zonars

Assistant Vice Presidents
Diane Abbatecola, Laurey Allis, Vin Bissoondial, Meg Bowen, James Bruce-Gardyne, Leila Buckjune, Andrew Butterfield,
Karen Christian, Andree Corroon, Edward Cullen, Peter Daly, Ellen de Boer, Noah Durham, Elizabeth Edwards,
Monique Foster, Constantine Frangos, Christopher Gaillard, Lee White Galvis, Jennifer Garvin, Chris Giacoppo,
Samantha Gilbert, Christine Grounds, Lynda Havell, Anya Herz, Sachiko Hori, Mary Horner, Val Hoyt, Kitty Ijams,
John Iszard, Heather Johnson, Jennifer Kaplan, Heakyum Kim, Sharon Kim, Lydia Fitler Kimball, Catherine Leonhard,
Lisa Klitses, Jennifer Kornicki, Jamie Krass, Jeffrey Kuduk, Chantal Lakatos, Susan Lewis, Sarah Lidsey, Betty Lin, Gabriela Lobo,
Marla Lombard, Robert, Looker, Vredy Lytsman, Andrew Massad, Deborah McLeod, Karin McQuade,
Victoria Meistrell, Miles Morris, Shira Nichaman, Jodi Norrison, Brett O'Connor, Robert O'Rourke, Gil Perez, Peter Petrou,
Elisabeth Poole, Susan Ravenscroft, Peter Rohowsky, Michael Samet, Elizabeth Sarnoff, Stacey Sayer, Mia Schläppi,
Natasha Schlesinger, Mary Sheridan, Riya Takaya, Kelly Troester, Juan Varez, Eric J. Wagensonner, Allison Whiting,
Laura Whitman, Sarah Wong

Dress photography by Christie's in-house photographer: David Schlegel
Dress Stylist: Christopher Fey
Manaquins Courtesy of Barney's New York

Creative Director: Lynda Havell
Designer: Sasha Swetschinski
Christie's Creative Services, New York

Produced and printed in England
By Christie's International plc
Media Division
21-25 South Lambeth Road, London SW8 1SX Tel: (44 171) 582 1188